WEBSTER'S
CONCISE
DICTIONARY OF
GRAMMAR

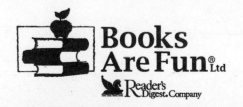

Books
Are Fun®
Ltd.

Reader's
Digest. Company

A

This edition published 2004 for Books Are Fun by Geddes & Grosset,
David Dale House, New Lanark ML11 9DJ, Scotland

© 2004 Geddes & Grosset

ISBN 1 84205 419 8

Printed and bound in Poland, OZGraf S.A.

A

a *see* **indefinite article**.

a-, an-
A prefix derived from Greek meaning "not," "without." Older words using it include agnostic, anarchy, anonymous. Several modern words have been formed using it, as in apolitical, asexual, atypical.

abbreviation
A shortened form of words, usually used as a space-saving technique and becoming increasingly common in modern usage. Abbreviations cause problems with regard to punctuation. The common question asked is whether the letters of an abbreviation should be separated by periods. In modern usage the tendency is to omit periods from abbreviations. This is most true of abbreviations involving initial capital letters, as in FBI, IRS, NBC, and USA. In such cases periods should definitely not be used if one or some of the initial letters do not belong to a full word. Thus "television" is abbreviated to TV and "intravenous" to IV.

There are usually no periods in abbreviations involving the first and last letters of a word (contractions)—Dr, Mr, Rd, St—but this is a matter of taste.

An abbreviation involving the first few letters of a word, as in "Prof" (Professor), is the most likely to a have period, as in "Feb." (February), but again this is now a matter of taste.

Plurals of abbreviations are mostly formed by adding lower-case *s*, as in Drs, JPs, TVs. Note the absence of apostrophes. *See also* ACRONYMS.

ablative
A case in Latin grammar that expressed "by, with, or from." In English this case does not exist, prepositional phrases being used in its place.

-able

A suffix meaning "that can be," as in laughable, readable, washable. *See* ADJECTIVE.

abstract noun

A noun that is the name of a thing that cannot be touched but that refers to a quality, concept, or idea. Examples of abstract nouns include "anger," "beauty," "courage," "danger," "envy," "fear," "greed," "hospitality," "ignorance," "Judaism," "kudos," "loyalty," "Marxism," "need," "obstinacy," "pain," "quality," "resistance," "safety," "truth," "unworthiness," "vanity," "wisdom," "xenophobia," "youth," "zeal." *See also* CONCRETE NOUN.

accent

(1) A regional or individual way of speaking or pronouncing words, as in "a Texan accent."

(2) A word meaning "emphasis," as in "In hotel the accent is on the second syllable of the word" or "In fashion this year the accent is on longer skirts."

(3) Any of certain symbols used on some foreign words adopted into English. In modern usage, which has a tendency to punctuate less than formerly was the case, accents are frequently omitted. For example, an actor's part in a play is now usually spelt "role" but originally it was spelt "rôle," the accent on *o* being called a circumflex. The accent is most likely to be retained if it affects the pronunciation. Thus "cliché" and "passé" usually retain the acute accent, as it is called, on the *e*. On the other hand, the accent known as the cedilla is frequently omitted from beneath the *c* in words such as "façade/facade," although it is there to indicate that the *c* is soft, pronounced like an *s*, rather than a hard sound, pronounced like a *k*. The grave accent is retained in English in some words and phrases derived from French, as *mise en scène*.

accusative

A case in Latin grammar, the equivalent of OBJECTIVE CASE. It is sometimes used in English instead of objective.

acronym

A word that, like some ABBREVIATIONS, is formed from the initial letters of several words. Unlike abbreviations, however, acronyms are pronounced as words rather than as just a series of letters. For example, OPEC (Organization of Petroleum Producing Countries) is pronounced *o-pek* and is thus an acronym, unlike USA (United States of America), which is pronounced as a series of letters and not as a word (*oo-sa* or *yoo-sa*) and is thus an abbreviation.

Acronyms are written without periods, as in UNESCO (United Nations Educational, Scientific, and Cultural Organization). Mostly acronyms are written in capital letters, as in NASA (National Aeronautics and Space Administration). However, very common acronyms, such as Anzac (Australian and New Zealand Army Corps), are written with just an initial capital, the rest of the letters being lower-case.

Acronyms that refer to a piece of scientific or technical equipment are written like ordinary words, in lower-case letters, as laser (light amplification by simulated emission of radiation).

active voice

One of the two voices that verbs are divided into, the other being PASSIVE VOICE. In verbs in the active voice, commonly called **active verbs**, the subject of the verb performs the action described by the verb. Thus, in the sentence "The boy threw the ball," "threw" is in the active voice since the subject of the verb (the boy) is doing the throwing. Similarly, in the sentence "Her mother was driving the car," "driving" is in the active voice since it is the subject of the sentence (her mother) that is doing the driving. Similarly, in the sentence "We saw the cows in the field," "saw" is the active voice since it is the subject of the sentence (we) that is doing the seeing.

acute accent

A mark placed over some letters in certain languages, such as French, to indicate vowel length, vowel quality, pronunciation, etc. It is found in English in some words that have been borrowed from the French, as in "fiancé" and "café," to indicate pronunciation.

-ade

A suffix meaning "fruit drink," as in lemonade.

adjectival clause

A kind of SUBORDINATE CLAUSE that describes or modifies a noun or pronoun. It is better known by the name RELATIVE CLAUSE.

adjective

A word that describes or gives information about a noun or pronoun. It is said to qualify a noun or pronoun since it limits the word it describes in some way, by making it more specific. Thus, adding the adjective "red" to "book" limits "book," since it means we can forget about books of any other color. Similarly, adding "large" to "book" limits it, since it means we can forget about books of any other size.

Adjectives tell us something about the color, size, number, quality, or classification of a noun or pronoun, as in "purple curtains," "jet-black hair," "bluish eyes"; "tiny baby," "large houses," "biggish gardens," "massive estates"; "five children," "twenty questions," "seventy-five books"; "sad people," "joyful occasions," "delicious food," "civil engineering," "nuclear physics," "modern languages," "Elizabethan drama."

Several adjectives may modify one noun or pronoun, as in "the small, black cat," "an enormous, red-brick, Victorian house." The order in which they appear is flexible and can vary according to the emphasis one wishes to place on the various adjectives. However, a common sequence is size, quality, color, and classification, as in "a small, beautiful, pink wild rose" and "a large, ugly, gray office building."

Adjectives do not change their form. They remain the same whether the noun to which they refer is singular or plural, or masculine or feminine.

All the above examples of adjectives come before the noun, but not all adjectives do so. For information on the position of adjectives *see* ATTRIBUTIVE ADJECTIVE, PREDICATIVE ADJECTIVE, POST-MODIFIER.

Many adjectives are formed from either the past participles of verbs, and so end in *-ed*, or from the present participles and so end in *-ing*. Examples of adjectives ending in *-ed* include "annoyed," "blackened," "colored," "damaged," "escaped," "faded," "guarded," "heated," "identified," "jaded," "knotted," "labeled," "mixed," "numbered," "opened," "pleated," "recorded," "satisfied," "taped," "used," "varied," "walled," "yellowed," "zoned." Examples of adjectives ending in *-ing* include "amusing," "boring," "captivating," "demanding," "enchanting," "falling," "grating," "horrifying," "identifying," "jarring," "kneeling," "laboring," "manufacturing," "nursing," "operating," "parting," "quivering," "racing," "satisfying," "telling," "undermining," "worrying," "yielding," "zigzagging."

Several adjectives end in *-ical* and are formed by adding *-al* to certain nouns ending in *-ic*. Examples include "arithmetical," "comical," "critical," "cynical," "fanatical," "logical," "magical," "musical," "mystical," and "skeptical." Sometimes the adjectives ending in *-ical* are formed from nouns that end in *-ics*. These include "acoustical," "ethical," "hysterical," "statistical," and "tropical." Several adjectives end in *-ic* and are formed from nouns ending in *-ics*. These include "acoustic," "acrobatic," "aerobic," "athletic," "economic," "electronic," "genetic," "gymnastic," "histrionic," and "linguistic."

Other common adjectival endings include *-ful*, as in "beautiful," "dreadful," "eventful," "graceful," "hateful," "tearful," and "youthful." They also include *-less*, as in "clueless," "graceless," "hatless," "meaningless," and "sunless."

Many adjectives end in *-able* and many end in *-ible*. There are often spelling problems with such adjectives. The following adjectives are likely to be misspelt:

Some adjectives ending in *-able*:

abominable	durable	objectionable
acceptable	enviable	operable
adaptable	excitable	palpable
adorable	excusable	pleasurable
advisable	expendable	preferable
agreeable	foreseeable	readable
amiable	forgettable	recognizable
approachable	forgivable	regrettable
available	healable	renewable
bearable	hearable	reputable
beatable	immovable	sizable
believable	impassable	stoppable
blamable	impeccable	tenable
calculable	implacable	tolerable
capable	impracticable	transferable

changeable	impressionable	understandable
comfortable	indescribable	unmistakable
commendable	indispensable	usable
conceivable	inimitable	variable
definable	insufferable	viable
delectable	lamentable	washable
demonstrable	manageable	wearable
dependable	measurable	winnable
desirable	memorable	workable
discreditable	namable	
disreputable	non-flammable	

Some adjectives ending in *-ible*:

accessible	divisible	perceptible
admissible	edible	permissible
audible	exhaustible	possible
collapsible	expressible	repressible
combustible	fallible	reproducible
compatible	feasible	resistible
comprehensible	flexible	responsible
contemptible	forcible	reversible
credible	gullible	risible
defensible	indelible	sensible
destructible	intelligible	susceptible
digestible	irascible	tangible
discernible	negligible	visible

See also COMPARISON OF ADJECTIVES, COMPOUNDS, DEMONSTRATIVE DETERMINERS, DETERMINER, FIRST PERSON, INTERROGATIVE ADJECTIVE, SECOND PERSON, and THIRD PERSON.

adverb

A word that adds to our information about a VERB, as in "work rapidly"; about an ADJECTIVE, as in "an extremely beautiful young woman"; or about another adverb, as in "sleeping very soundly." Adverbs are said to modify the words to which they apply since they limit the words in some way and make them more specific. Thus, adding "slowly" to "walk," as in "They walked slowly down the hill," limits the verb "walk" since all other forms of "walk," such as "quickly," "lazily," etc., have been discarded.

There are several different kinds of adverb, categorized according to the information they provide about the word they modify. They include adverbs of time, adverbs of place, adverbs of manner, adverbs of degree, adverbs of frequency, adverbs of probability, adverbs of duration, and interrogative adverbs.

An **adverb of time** tells us when something happened, and they include such words as "now," "then," "later," "soon," "afterward," "yesterday," etc., as in "He is due to arrive now," "I will call you later," "She had a rest and went out afterward," "They left yesterday."

An **adverb of place** tells us where something happened. Adverbs of place include such words as "there," "here," "somewhere," "anywhere," "thereabouts," "overseas," "outdoors," "overhead," "underground," "hither and thither," etc., as in "I haven't been there," "They couldn't see her anywhere," "His family live overseas," and "We heard a noise overhead."

An **adverb of manner** tells us how something happens, and they include a wide range of possibilities. Frequently adverbs in this category are formed by adding -*ly* to an adjective. Examples of these include:

adjective	adverb	adjective	adverb
anxious	anxiously	mean	meanly
bad	badly	narrow	narrowly
cautious	cautiously	pale	palely
dear	dearly	quick	quickly
elegant	elegantly	rare	rarely
fashionable	fashionably	soothing	soothingly
gracious	graciously	tough	toughly
hot	hotly	unwilling	unwillingly
interested	interestedly	vain	vainly
joking	jokingly	weak	weakly
lame	lamely		

Some adjectives have to be modified in some way before the suffix -*ly* is added to form the adverbs. For example, in adjectives ending in -*y*, the *y* changes to *i* before -*ly* is added. Examples of these include:

adjective	adverb	adjective	adverb
angry	angrily	happy	happily
busy	busily	merry	merrily
creepy	creepily	pretty	prettily

dry	drily	**shaky**	shakily
easy	easily	tacky	tackily
funny	funnily	weary	wearily

Note the exceptions "shyly," "slyly," "wryly."

Adjectives ending in -*e* frequently drop the *e* before adding -*ly*. Examples of these include:

adjective	adverb	adjective	adverb
able	ably	peaceable	peaceably
feeble	feebly	true	truly
gentle	gently	unintelligible	unintelligibly

Suffixes other than -*ly* that may be added to adjectives to form adverbs of manner include -*ward*, as in backward, heavenward; -*ways*, as in edgeways, sideways; -*wise*, as in clockwise, moneywise.

Some adverbs of manner may take the same form as the adjectives to which they correspond. These include "fast," "hard," "solo," "straight," "wrong," as in "She took the wrong book" and "Don't get me wrong."

An **adverb of degree** tells us the degree, extent, or intensity of something that happens, and they include "hugely," "immensely," "moderately," "adequately," "greatly," "strongly," "tremendously," "profoundly," "totally," "entirely," "perfectly," "partially," "practically," "virtually," "almost," as in "They enjoyed the show hugely," "The office was not adequately equipped," "We strongly disapprove of such behavior," "He was totally unaware of the facts," "They are virtually penniless."

An **adverb of frequency** is used to tell us how often something happens, and they include "never," "rarely," "seldom," "infrequently," "occasionally," "periodically," "intermittently," "sometimes," "often," "frequently," "regularly," "normally," "always," "constantly," "continually," as in "She never eats breakfast," "We go to the movies occasionally," "He goes to the dentist regularly," "Normally they travel by bus," "He is in pain constantly."

An **adverb of probability** tells us how often something happens, and they include "probably," "possibly," "conceivably," "perhaps," "maybe," "presumably," "hopefully," "definitely," "certainly," "indubitably," "doubtless," as in "You will probably see them there," "He may conceivably pass the test this time," "Presumably they know that she is leaving," "Hopefully the news will be good," "I am definitely not going," "He is indubitably a criminal."

An **adverb of duration** tells us how long something takes or lasts, and they include "briefly," "temporarily," "long," "indefinitely," "always," "permanently," "forever," as in "We stopped briefly for coffee," "Have you known her long?", "Her face is permanently disfigured," "They have parted forever."

An **adverb of emphasis** adds emphasis to the action described by the verb, and they include "absolutely," "certainly," "positively," "quite," "really," "simply," "just," as in "They absolutely detest each other," "He positively adores her," "She really wants to be forgiven," "I simply must go now."

An **interrogative adverb** asks questions, and they include "where," "when," "how," and "why," as in "Where are you going?", "When will you be back?", "How will you get there?", "Why have they asked you to go?" They are placed at the beginning of sentences, and such sentences always end with a question mark.

adverbial clause

A subordinate clause that modifies the main or principal clause by adding information about time, place, concession, condition, manner, purpose, and result. Adverbial clauses usually follow the main clause but most of them can be put in front of the main clause for reasons of emphasis or style.

An **adverbial clause of time** indicates the time of an event and is introduced by a conjunction such as "after," "as," "as soon as," "before," "once," "since," "the minute," "the moment," "till," "until," "when," "whenever," "while," "whilst," as in "He left after dinner was over," "She arrived as I was leaving," "Once I recognized him I spoke to him," "I recognized him the minute I saw him," "We won't know until tomorrow" and "The thief ran away when he saw the police."

An **adverbial clause of place** indicates the location of an event and is introduced by a conjunction such as "where," "wherever," or "everywhere," as in "He was miserable where he was," "They left it where they found it," "Wherever I went I saw signs of poverty," and "Everywhere she goes she causes trouble."

An **adverbial clause of concession** contains a fact that contrasts in some way with the main clause and is introduced by a CONJUNCTION such as "although," "even though," "though," "whereas," "while," as in "I have to admire his speech, although I disagree with what he said," "He does his best at school work even though he is not very good at it," and "While I myself do not like him I can understand why he is popular."

An **adverbial clause of condition** deals with possible situations and is introduced by the conjunctions "if," "only if," "unless," "as long as," "providing," "provided," as in "If you had kept quiet they would not have known about the event," "We cannot go unless we get permission," "They can leave only if they have finished their work," and "Provided he is feeling better he can go home." Inversion can be used in such clauses instead of a conjunction, as in "Had you been present you would have been most amused," and "Had he any sense he would leave now."

An **adverbial clause of manner** describes the way that someone behaves or the way in which something is done, and is introduced by a conjunction such as "as," "as if," "as though," "like," "the way," as in "Why does he behave as he does?", "He slurred his speech as though he were drunk," and "He looked at her as if he hated her."

An **adverbial clause of purpose** indicates the intention someone has when doing something and is introduced by a conjunction such as "to," "in order to," "so as to," "so," "so that," as in "He did that just to upset her," "They will have to work long hours in order to make that amount of money," "They started to run so as to get home before it rained," and "The firm reduced the number of staff in order that they might avoid bankruptcy."

An **adverbial clause of reason** explains why something happens or is done and is introduced by a conjunction such as "because," "since," or "as," as in "We didn't go because the car broke down," "As it was raining we had the party indoors," and "Since he has broken the school rules he should be punished."

An **adverbial clause of result** indicates the result of an event or situation and is introduced by the conjunctions "so" or "so that," as in "He fell awkwardly so that he broke his leg" and "She stumbled over her words so that the audience had difficulty understanding her." *See* COMPARISON OF ADVERBS and COMPOUNDS.

aero-

A prefix meaning "air," as in aerobics, aerodynamics, and aerospace, or "aircraft," as in aerodrome, aeronaut.

affix

An element that is added to a base or root word to form another word. Affixes can be in the form of prefixes or suffixes. A **prefix** is an affix that is added to the beginning of a word. Thus *audio* in "audiovisual" is both a prefix and an affix. A **suffix** is an affix that is added to the end of a word. Thus *-aholic* in "workaholic" is a suffix and an affix.

agent noun

A noun that refers to someone who is the "doer" of the action of a verb. It is usually spelt ending in either *-er*, as "inquirer," or in *-or*, as in "investigator" and "supervisor," but frequently either of these endings is acceptable, as "adviser/advisor."

agreement *or* concord

The agreeing of two or more elements in a clause or sentence, i.e. they take the same number, person, or gender. In English the most common form of agreement is that between subject and verb, and this usually involves NUMBER AGREEMENT. This means that singular nouns are usually accompanied by singular verbs, as in "She looks well," "He is working late," and "The boy has passed the test," and that plural nouns are usually accompanied by plural verbs, as in "They look well," "They are working late," and "The boys have passed the test."

Problems arise when the noun in question can be either singular or plural, e.g. "audience," "committee," "crowd," "family," "government," "group." Such nouns take a singular verb if the user is regarding the people or items referred to by the noun as a group, as in "The family is moving house," or as individuals, as in "The family are quarreling over where to go on holiday."

Compound subjects, that is two or more nouns acting as the subject, whether singular or plural, joined with "and," are used with a plural noun, as in "My friend and I are going to the movies tonight" and "James and John are leaving today," unless the two nouns together represent a single concept, as "brandy and soda," in which case the verb is in the singular, as in "Brandy and soda is his favorite drink" and "salami and ham" in "Salami and ham is the only sandwich filling available."

In cases where two or more singular nouns acting as the subject are connected with such phrases as "as well as," "together with," and "plus," as in "His mother, as well as his father, is away from home" and "The apartment, together with the house, is up for sale," the verb is in the singular.

Indefinite pronouns such as "anyone," "everyone," "no one," "someone," "either," "neither" are singular and should be followed by a singular verb, as in "Each of the apartments is self-contained," "Everyone is welcome," "No one is allowed in without a ticket," and "Neither is quite what I am looking for."

When the subject is a singular noun, which is separated from the verb by a number of plural nouns, as in "a list of dates and times of the next concerts," the verb is in the singular because "list" is singular, as in "A list of dates and times of the next concerts is available."

Agreement with reference to both number and gender affects pronouns, as in "She blames herself," "He could have kicked himself," and "They asked themselves why they had gotten involved." Problems arise when the pronoun is indefinite and so the sex of the person is unspecified. Formerly in such cases the masculine pronouns were assumed to be neutral and so "Each of the students was asked to hand in his work" was considered quite acceptable. The rise of feminism has led to a questioning of this assumption and alternatives have been put forward. These include "Each of the students was asked to hand in his/her (or his or her) work," but some people feel that this is clumsy. Another alternative is "Each of the students was asked to hand in their work." Although it is ungrammatical, this convention is becoming quite acceptable in modern usage. To avoid both the clumsiness of the former and the ungrammaticalness of the latter, it is possible to cast the whole sentence in the plural, as in "All the students were asked to hand in their work."

agro-, agri-

A prefix derived from Greek meaning "field," as in agriculture, agribusiness, agrobiology, agrochemicals.

-aholic

A suffix meaning "addicted to," formed on ANALOGY with "alcoholic," as in workaholic, shopaholic. It sometimes becomes -oholic, as in chocoholic.

allegory

A kind of story that has deeper significance as well as the obvious surface meaning of the story. It is usually used to get a moral message across symbolically. Two of the most famous allegories in English literature are *The Pilgrim's Progress* by John Bunyan (1628–88) and *The Faerie Queene* by Edmund Spenser (*c*.1552–99).

alliteration

A figure of speech in which a sequence of words begin with the same letter or sound, as in "Round and round the rugged rocks the ragged rascal ran" and "Peter Piper picked a peck of pickled peppers." The given examples are both tongue-twisters but alliteration is frequently used by poets for literary effect as in a "red, red rose."

also

An adverb that should not be used as a CONJUNCTION instead of "and." Thus sentences such as "Please send me some apples, also some pears" are grammatically incorrect.

although

A conjunction that is used to introduce a subordinate adverbial clause of concession, as in "They are very happy although they are poor," meaning "Despite the fact they are poor they are happy." "Though" or "even though" can be substituted for "although," as in "They are very happy even though they are poor." *See* ADVERBIAL CLAUSE and CONJUNCTION.

ambi-

A prefix derived from Greek meaning "two," "both," as in ambidextrous, ambivalent.

an *see* **indefinite article**.

an- *see* **a-**.

-ana

A suffix meaning "things associated with," as in Victoriana, Americana.

anacoluthon

A FIGURE OF SPEECH that refers to a change of construction in a sentence before the original structure is complete, as in "My feeling is—but you must decide for yourself—how long did you say you have?" Anacoluthon is usually found in spoken English when someone is thinking aloud. Unlike many figures of speech, it is usually used accidentally rather than for literary or rhetorical effect.

anadiplosis

A FIGURE OF SPEECH that refers to the repetition of a word or group at the end of one phrase or sentence and the beginning of the next for literary effect, as in "sit and think about the past—the past which had been so warm and happy."

analogy

A FIGURE OF SPEECH, rather like the SIMILE, in which there is an inference of a resemblance between two items that are being compared, as in "Mary's parties are a bit like Christmas—much looked forward to but often a bit of a disappointment."

anastrophe

A FIGURE OF SPEECH that refers to an inversion of the usual order of words in a sentence or phrase for emphasis, or literary or rhetorical effect, as in "Many a foreign dawn has he seen."

and

A conjunction that is called a coordinating conjunction because it joins elements of language that are of equal status. The elements may be words, as in "cows and horses," "John and James," "provide wine and beer"; phrases, as in "working hard and playing hard" and "trying to look after her children and her elderly parents"; clauses, as in "John has decided to emigrate and his brother has decided to join him" and "He has lost his job and he now has no money." When a coordinating conjunction is used, the subject of the second clause can sometimes be omitted if it is the same as the subject of the first clause, as in "They have been forced to sell the house and are very sad about it." *See* CONJUNCTION.

The use of and at the beginning of a sentence is disliked by many people. It should be used only for deliberate effect, as in "And then he saw the monster," or in informal contexts.

Other coordinating conjunctions include "but," "or," "yet," "both . . . and," "either . . . or," and "neither . . . nor," as in "poor but honest" and "the blue dress or the green one."

Anglo-

A prefix meaning "English," as in Anglo-Irish, Anglo-Indian.

ante-

A prefix derived from Latin meaning "before," as in antedate, ante-natal, anteroom.

antecedent

A term that refers to the noun or noun phrase in a main clause to which a relative pronoun in a relative clause refers back. Thus in the sentence "People who live dangerously frequently get hurt," "people" is an antecedent. Similarly, in the sentence "The child identified the old man who attacked her," "the old man" is the antecedent. *See* RELATIVE CLAUSE.

anthropo-

A prefix derived from Greek meaning "human being," as in anthropoid, anthropology.

anti-

A prefix derived from Greek meaning "against." It is used in many words that have been established in the language for a long time, as in antidote and antipathy, but it has also been used to form modern words, such as antiballistic, antifreeze, anti-inflationary, anti-nuclear, anti-Semitism.

anticlimax

A FIGURE OF SPEECH in which there is a sudden descent from the lofty to the ridiculous or the trivial, as in "She went home in a flood of tears and a taxi." A well-known 19th-century example is in the couplet:
"And thou, Dalhousie, the great god of war,
Lieutenant-general to the earl of Mar."

antiphrasis

A FIGURE OF SPEECH in which a word or phrase is used in a sense
that is opposite to the accepted sense. It is often used to achieve
an ironic or humorous effect, as in "His mother is ninety years
young today." Young is usually associated with youth but here it is
associated with old age.

antithesis

A FIGURE OF SPEECH in which contrasting ideas are balanced for
effect, as in "We need money, not advice," "More haste, less
speed," and "Marry at haste, repent at leisure." It is a common
figure of speech in literature, as in Alexander Pope's "To err is
human, to forgive divine" and John Milton's "Better to reign in
hell than to serve in heaven."

antonomasia

A FIGURE OF SPEECH indicating the use of a personal name or proper
name to anyone belonging to a class or group, as in "John is such
an Einstein that the other members of the class are in awe of him,"
where the meaning is that "John has such a brilliant mind that the
other members of the class are in awe of him."

antonym

A word that is the opposite of another word. Thus "black" is an
antonym for "white," "cowardly" is an antonym for "courageous,"
"dull" is an antonym for "bright," and "fast" is an antonym for
"slow."

any

A pronoun that may take either a singular or plural verb, depending on the context. When a singular noun is used, a singular verb is
used, as in "Is any of the cloth still usable?" "Are any of the children
coming?" When a plural noun is used, either a plural or a singular
verb can be used, the singular verb being more formal, as in "Did
you ask if any of his friends were/was there?"

anyone

A pronoun that should be used with a singular verb, as in "Has
anyone seen my book?" and "Is anyone coming to the lecture?" It
should also be followed, where relevant, by a singular, not plural,

personal pronoun or possessive adjective, as in "Has anyone left his/her book?" Because this construction, which avoids the sexist "his," is considered by many people to be clumsy, there is a growing tendency to use "their" and be ungrammatical.

aposiopesis

A FIGURE OF SPEECH in which words are omitted or there is a sudden breaking off for dramatic effect, as in "The door slowly opened and . . ." and "There was the noise of gunshot and then . . . ."

apostrophe[1]

A FIGURE OF SPEECH that takes the form of a rhetorical address to an absent or dead person or to a personified thing, as in "O Romeo! Romeo! wherefore art thou, Romeo?" and "Oh Peace, why have you deserted us?"

apostrophe[2]

A form of punctuation that is mainly used to indicate possession. Many spelling errors center on the position of the apostrophe in relation to *s*.

Possessive nouns are usually formed by adding *'s* to the singular noun, as in "the girl's mother" and "Peter's car"; by adding an apostrophe to plural nouns that end in *s*, as in "all the teachers' cars"; by adding *'s* to irregular plural nouns that do not end in *s*, as in "women's shoes."

In the possessive form of a name or singular noun that ends in *s*, *x*, or *z*, the apostrophe may or may not be followed by *s*. In words of one syllable the final *s* is usually added, as in "James's house," "the fox's lair," "Roz's dress." The final *s* is most frequently omitted in names, particularly in names of three or more syllables, as in "Euripides' plays." In many cases the presence or absence of final *s* is a matter of convention.

The apostrophe is also used to indicate omitted letters in contracted forms of words, as in "can't" and "you've." They are sometimes used to indicate missing century numbers in dates, as in "the '60s and '70s," but are not used at the end of decades, etc., as in "1960s," not "1960's."

Generally apostrophes are no longer used to indicate omitted letters in shortened forms that are in common use, as in "phone" and "flu."

Apostrophes are often omitted wrongly in modern usage, particularly in the media and by advertisers, as in "womens hairdressers," "childrens portions." In addition, apostrophes are frequently added erroneously (as in "potato's for sale" and "Beware of the dog's"). This is partly because people are unsure about when and when not to use them and partly because of a modern tendency to punctuate as little as possible.

apposition

A term for a noun or a phrase that provides further information about another noun or phrase. Both nouns and phrases refer to the same person or thing. In the phrase "Paula Jones, our managing director," "Paula Jones," and "our managing director" are said to be in apposition. Similarly, in the phrase "his cousin, the chairman of the firm," "his cousin" and "the chairman of the firm" are in apposition.

arch-

A prefix derived from Greek meaning "chief," as in archbishop, archduke, arch-enemy.

-arch

A suffix derived from Greek meaning "chief, ruler," as in anarchy, hierarchy, monarchy.

-arian

A suffix derived from Latin meaning, in one of its senses, "a supporter of," as in vegetarian, or "one connected with," as in antiquarian, librarian.

article *see* definite article *and* indefinite article.

as

A conjunction that can introduce either a subordinate adverbial clause of time, as in "I caught sight of him as I was leaving," a subordinate adverbial clause of manner, as in "He acted as he promised," and a subordinate adverbial clause of reason, as in "As it's Saturday he doesn't have to work." It is also used in the as.... as construction, as in "She doesn't play as well as her sister does."

The construction may be followed by a subject pronoun or an object pronoun, according to sense. In the sentence "She plays as well as he," which is a slightly shortened form of "She plays as well as he does," "he" is a subject pronoun. In informal English the subject pronoun often becomes an object pronoun, as in "She plays as well as him." In the sentence "They hate their father as much as her," "her" is an object pronoun and the sentence means "They hate their father as much as they hate her," but in the sentence "They hate their father as much as she," "she" is a subject pronoun and the sentence means "They hate their father as much as she does." *See* ADVERBIAL CLAUSE and CONJUNCTION.

assonance
A figure of speech in which vowel sounds are repeated to give a half-rhyme effect, as in "with gun, drum, trumpet, blunderbuss, and thunder."

astro-
A prefix derived from Greek meaning "star," as in astrology, astronomy, astronaut, astrophysics.

asyndeton
A figure of speech referring to the omission of conjunctions for dramatic or literary effect, as in "I came, I saw, I conquered" and "He entered, he looked around, he left."

-athon, -thon
A suffix meaning "large scale or long-lasting contest or event," as in swimathon, telethon. These words are formed on analogy with the Greek derived word marathon, and they often refer to events undertaken for charity.

attributive adjective
A term for an adjective that is placed immediately before the noun that it qualifies. In the phrases "a red dress," "the big house", and "an enjoyable evening," "red," "big," and "enjoyable" are attributive adjectives.

audio-

A word derived from Latin meaning "hear." It is found in several words that have been established in the language for a long time, as in auditory, audition, but it is also used to form many modern words, as in audiotape, audio-cassette, and audiovisual.

auto-

A prefix derived from Greek meaning "of or by itself," as in autobiography and autograph. It is also used to refer to things that work by themselves "automatically," as in automobile, autocue, automaton, and to things that have to do with cars, as in automobiles, autosport, autotheft.

auxiliary verb

A verb that is used in forming tenses, moods, and voices of other verbs. These include "be," "do," and "have."

The verb "to be" is used as an **auxiliary verb** with the *-ing* form of the main verb to form the continuous present tense, as in "They are living overseas just now" and "We were thinking of going on vacation but we changed our minds."

The verb "to be" is used as an auxiliary verb with the past participle of the main verb to form the passive voice, as in "Her hands were covered in blood" and "These toys are manufactured in China."

The verb "to have" is used as an auxiliary verb along with the past participle of the main verb to form the perfect tenses, as in "They have filled the post," "She had realized her mistake," and "They wished that they had gone earlier."

The verb "to be" is used as an auxiliary verb along with the main verb to form negative sentences, as in "She is not accepting the position." The verb "to do" is used as an auxiliary verb along with the main verb to form negative sentences, as in "He does not believe her." It is also used along with the main verb to form questions, as in "Does he know that she's gone?" and to form sentences in which the verb is emphasized, as in "She *does* want to go." *See* MODAL VERB.

B

back formation

The process of forming a new word by removing an element from an existing word. This is the reversal of the usual process since many words are formed by adding an element to a base or root word. Examples of back formation include "caretake" from "caretaker"; "donate" from "donation"; "eavesdrop" from "eavesdropper"; "enthuse" from "enthusiasm"; "intuit" from "intuition"; "liaise" from "liaison"; "reminisce" from "reminiscence"; "televise" from "television."

base

The basic uninflected form of a verb. It is found as the infinitive form, as in "to go" and "to take," and as the imperative form, as in "Go away!" and "Take it!" It is also the form that the verb in the present indicative tense takes, except for the third person singular, as in "I always go there on a Sunday" and "They go there regularly."

Base also refers to the basic element in word formation. In this sense it is also known as "root" or "stem." For example, in the word "infectious" "infect" is the base, in "indescribable" "describe" is the base and in "enthusiastic" "enthuse" is the base.

bathos

A figure of speech consisting of sudden descent from the lofty or noble to the ridiculous or trivial. This descent can be either intentional for comic or satiric effect, as in Alexander Pope's "When husbands or when lapdogs breathe their last," or it can be accidental, as in "She collected her children and her coat." Bathos and anticlimax mean the same. *See* ANTICLIMAX.

be *see* **auxiliary verb**.

because

A conjunction that introduces a subordinate adverbial clause of reason, as in "They sold the house because they are going overseas" and "Because she is bashful she never goes to parties." It is often used incorrectly in such constructions as "The reason they went away is because they were bored." This should be rephrased as either "The reason that they went away is that they were bored" or "They went away because they were bored." *See* ADVERBIAL CLAUSE.

before

A word that can either be a preposition, an adverb, or a conjunction. As a preposition it means either "coming or going in front of in time," as in "He was the chairman before this one," or coming or going in front of in place, as in "She went before him into the restaurant." As an adverb it means "at a time previously," as in "I told you before" and "He has been married before." As a conjunction it introduces a subordinate adverbial clause of time, as in "The guests arrived before she was ready for them" and "Before I knew it they had arrived." *See* ADVERBIAL CLAUSE.

bi-

A prefix derived from Latin meaning "two," as in bicycle, bifocal, bilingual, binoculars, bisect. Bi- forms words in English in which it means "half," and other words in which it means "twice." This can give rise to confusion in such words as biweekly and bimonthly, where there are two possible sets of meanings. Biweekly can mean either "every two weeks" or "twice a week" so that one would not be able to be certain about the frequency of a "biweekly publication." Similarly, a "bimonthly publication" might appear either twice a month or once every two months.

biblio-

A prefix derived from Greek meaning "book," as in bibliophile (a person who is fond of or collects books) and bibliography.

bio-

A prefix derived from Greek meaning "life or living material," as in biography, biology, biochemistry, biodegradable, biosphere, biopsy.

blend

A word that is formed by the merging of two other words or elements, as in "brunch" from "breakfast" and "lunch"; "camcorder" from "camera" and "recorder"; "chocoholic" from "chocolate" and "alcoholic"; "motel" from "motor" and "hotel"; "smog" from "smoke" and "fog"; "televangelist" from "television" and "evangelist."

bold *or* bold face

A typeface that is thick and black. It is used for emphasis or to highlight certain words. The headwords, or entry words, in this book are set in bold type.

book titles

These can cause problems as to punctuation. How they are treated in publications, business reports, etc., depends largely on the house style of the firm concerned. However, they are generally written in documents, letters, etc., as they appear on their title pages, that is with the first letter of the first word and of the following main words of the title in capital letters, and those of words of lesser importance, such as the articles, prepositions, and coordinate conjunctions, in lower-case letters, as in The Guide to Yoga, Hope for the Best, and In the Middle of Life.

Some people, and some house-style manuals, prefer to put the titles in italic, as in *A Room with a View* and *A Guide to Dental Health*. Others prefer to put book titles in quotation marks, as in "Gardening for Beginners." Such a convention can make use of either single or double quotation marks. Thus either 'Desserts for the Summer' or "Desserts for the Summer" is possible provided that the writer is consistent throughout any one piece of writing. If the title of a book is mentioned in a piece of direct speech in quotation marks it goes within the opposite style of quotation marks from the piece in direct speech. Thus if the direct speech is within single quotation marks, the book title goes within double quotation marks, as in 'Have you read "Wuthering Heights" or are you not a Brontë fan?' If the direct speech is within double quotation marks, the book title goes between single quotation marks, as in "Would you say that 'Animal Farm' was your favorite Orwell novel?"

It is even quite common for book titles to appear in documents both in italic type and with quotation marks. To some extent the punctuation of book titles is a matter of choice as long as they are consistent, but there is a growing tendency to have as little punctuation as possible and to have as uncluttered a page as possible.

borrowing

The taking over into English of a word from a foreign language. Many words borrowed into English are totally assimilated as to spelling and pronunciation. Others remain obviously different and retain their own identity as to spelling or pronunciation, as *raison d'être*, borrowed from French. Many of them have been so long part of the English language, such as since the Norman Conquest of England, that they are no longer thought of as being foreign words. However the process goes on, and more recent borrowings include *glasnost* and *perestroika* from Russian.

French, Latin, and Greek have been the main sources of our borrowings over the centuries. However, we have borrowed extensively from other languages as well. These include Italian, from which we have borrowed many terms relating to music, art, and architecture. These include *piano*, *libretto*, *opera*, *soprano*, *tempo*, *corridor*, *fresco*, *niche*, *parapet*, and *grotto*, as well as many food terms, such as *pizza*, *macaroni*, *pasta*, and *spaghetti*.

From the Dutch we have acquired many words relating to the sea and ships since they were a great sea-faring nation. These include *cruise*, *deck*, *skipper*, and *yacht*. Through the Dutch/Afrikaans connection we have borrowed *apartheid*, *boss*, and *trek*.

From German we have borrowed *dachshund*, *hamster*, *frankfurter*, *kindergarten*, and *waltz*, as well as some words relating to World War II, for example, *blitz*, *flak*, and *strafe*.

From Norse and the Scandinavian languages have come a wide variety of common words, such as *egg*, *dirt*, *glitter*, *kick*, *law*, *odd*, *skill*, *take*, *they*, *though*, as well as some more modern sporting terms such as *ski* and *slalom*.

From the Celtic languages have come *bannock*, *bog*, *brogue*, *cairn*, *clan*, *crag*, *slogan* and *whiskey*, and from Arabic have come *algebra*, *alkali*, *almanac*, *apricot*, *assassin*, *cipher*, *ghoul*, *hazard*, *mohair*, *safari*, *scarlet*, and *talisman*.

The Indian languages have provided us with many words, originally from the significant British presence there in the days of the British Empire. They include *bungalow*, *chutney*, *dinghy*, *dungarees*, *gymkhana*, *jungle*, *pundit*, and *shampoo*. In modern times there has been an increasing interest in Indian food and cookery, and words such as *biryani*, *curry*, etc., have come into the language.

From the South American languages have come *avocado*, *chocolate*, *chili*, *potato*, *tobacco*, and *tomato*. From Hebrew have come *alphabet*, *camel*, *cinnamon*, and *maudlin*, as well as more modern borrowings from Yiddish such as *bagel*, *chutzpah*, *schmaltz*, and *schmuck*.

From the Native American languages have come *anorak*, *kayak*, *raccoon*, and *toboggan*, and from the Aboriginal languages of Australia have come *boomerang* and *kangaroo*.

Judo, *bonsai*, *karaoke*, and *tycoon* have come from Japanese, *rattan* from Malay and *kung fu*, *sampan*, and *ginseng* from Chinese.

both

A word that can be used in several ways: as a determiner, as in "He broke both his arms" and "He lost both his sons in the war"; as a pronoun, as in "I don't mind which house we rent, I like them both" and "Neither of them work here. The boss sacked them both"; as a conjunction, as in "He both likes and admires her" and "She is both talented and honest." Both can sometimes be followed by "of." "Both their children are grown up" and "Both of their children are grown up" are both acceptable. Care should be taken to avoid using both unnecessarily. In the sentence "The two items are both identical," "both" is redundant.

-bound

A suffix meaning "confined or restricted," as in housebound, snowbound and spellbound. It can also mean "obligated," as in duty-bound.

brackets

A pair of characters that are used to enclose information that is in some way additional to a main statement. There are various shapes of brackets. Round brackets, more commonly called PARÉNTHESES, are the most common type. Square brackets are sometimes used to enclose information that is contained inside other information already in parentheses, as in "(Christopher Marlowe [1564–93] was a contemporary of Shakespeare)" or in a piece of writing where parentheses have already been used for some other purpose. Thus in a dictionary if parentheses are used to separate off the pronunciation, square brackets are sometimes used to separate off the etymologies.

Square brackets are also used for editorial comments in a scholarly work where the material within brackets is more of an intrusion to the flow of the main statement than is normally the case with material in parentheses.

Angle brackets and brace brackets tend to be used in more scholarly or technical contexts.

buildings

These can cause problems with regard to the style and punctuation of their names. The proper name attached to the building should have an initial capital, as should the common noun that may be part of it, as in the White House, the Chrysler Building, the Guggenheim Museum, and the Sears Tower.

businesses *and* organizations

These often cause style and punctuation problems with regard to their names or titles. In general, the initial letters of the main words of the title should be in capital letters and the words of lesser importance, such as the articles, coordinating conjunctions, and prepositions, should be in lower case, except when they are the first word of the title, as in "The Persian Carpet Company," "Kitchens for All" and "Capital Industrial Cleaners." Obviously, when the names of people are involved these should have initial capital letters, as in "Lopez and Brown."

but

A conjunction that connects two opposing ideas. It is a coordinating conjunction in that it connects two elements of equal status. The elements may be words, as in "not Paul but Leroy"; phrases, as in "working hard but not getting anywhere" and "trying to earn a living but not succeeding"; clauses, as in "He has arrived but his sister is late," "I know her but I have never met him" and "He likes reading but she prefers to watch TV." It should not be used when no element of contrast is present. Thus the following sentence should be rephrased, at least in formal English—"She is not professionally trained but taught herself." The two clauses are in fact agreeing, not disagreeing, with each other and so, strictly speaking, but should not be used.

The use of but at the beginning of a sentence is disliked by many people. It should be used only for deliberate effect or in informal contexts.

by-

A prefix meaning "subordinate," "secondary," "incidental," as in by-product, by-road, by-effect. It can also mean "around," as in by-pass.

C

capital letters

These are much less common than lower-case letters. They are used as the initial letters of proper nouns, the names of countries, rivers, mountains, cities, etc. Thus we find Canada, Mount Everest, River Nile, Chicago, etc. The first names and surnames of people have initial capital letters, as in Joel Black and Maria Brown. Initial capital letters are used for the days of the week, as in Tuesday and Wednesday, for the months of the year, as in May and October, public and religious holidays, as in Easter Sunday, Ramadan, and Hanukkah. Initial capital letters are used for the books of the Bible.

Points of the compass are spelt with an initial capital letter if they are part of a specific geographical feature or region, as in South Africa.

Initial capital letters are usually used in the titles of books. Only the main words are capitalized. The articles, prepositions, and coordinate conjunctions are left in lower case unless they form the first word of the title, as in *A Room with a View* and *For Whom the Bell Tolls*—*see* BOOK TITLES.

Initial capital letters are necessary in trade names, as in Tylenol, Jacuzzi, Xerox, and Kodak.

The first word in a sentence is spelt with a capital letter, as in "We heard them coming in. They made very little noise. However, we are light sleepers."

For capital letters in direct speech, *see* DIRECT SPEECH. For capital letters in abbreviations and acronyms, *see* ABBREVIATION and ACRONYM.

cardi-

A prefix derived from Greek meaning "heart," as in cardiology, cardiac.

cardinal number

The numbers one, two, three, four, etc., as opposed to ORDINAL NUM-BERS, which refer to numbers such as first, second, third, fourth, etc.

case

One of the forms in the DECLENSION of a noun, pronoun, or adjective in a sentence.

clause

A group of words containing a FINITE VERB, which forms part of a compound or complex sentence. See MAIN CLAUSE, SUBORDINATE CLAUSES, ADVERBIAL CLAUSE, NOUN CLAUSE, and RELATIVE CLAUSE.

clerihew

A humorous four-line light verse in which the first two lines rhyme with each other and the last two rhyme with each other. The clerihew was popularized by Edward Clerihew Bentley (1875–1956). It usually deals with a person named in the first line and then describes him or her in a humorous way, as in

> King Canute
> Had lots of loot
> He loved to gloat
> While petting his stoat.

cliché

A hackneyed stereotyped expression that is much over-used. Examples of clichés include "unaccustomed as I am to public speaking," "the light at the end of the tunnel," and "All's well that ends well."

collective noun

A singular noun that refers to a group of things or people. It is used when the whole group is being considered, as in "flock of sheep," "herd of cattle," "team of oxen," "shoal of herring," "covey of partridges," "unkindness of ravens," "gaggle of geese," "pride of lions," "mutation of thrushes," "exaltation of larks," "convocation of eagles."

colloquial

A term used to describe informal language, such as that found in informal conversation.

colon

A punctuation mark (:) that is used within a sentence to explain, interpret, clarify, or amplify what has gone before it. "The standard of high-school work here is extremely high: it is almost university standard," "The fuel bills are giving cause for concern: they are almost double last year's." "We have some new information: the allies have landed." A capital letter is not usually used after the colon in this context.

The colon is also used to introduce lists or long quotations, as in "The recipe says we need: tomatoes, peppers, zucchini, garlic, oregano, and basil," and "One of his favorite quotations was: 'If music be the food of love play on.'"

The colon is sometimes used with numerals, as in "7:30 a.m.," "11:22:99" and "a ratio of 7:3." It is used in the titles of some books, for example where there is a subtitle or explanatory title, as in "The Dark Years: the Economy in the 1930s."

In informal writing, the dash is sometimes used instead of the colon. Indeed the dash tends to be over-used for this purpose.

comma

A very common punctuation mark (,). In modern usage there is a tendency to adopt a system of minimal punctuation and the comma is one of the casualties of this new attitude. Most people use the comma considerably less frequently than was formerly the case.

However there are certain situations in which the comma is still commonly used. One of these concerns lists. The individual items in a series of three or more items are separated by commas. Whether a comma is put before the "and" which follows the second-last item is now a matter of choice. Some people dislike the use of a comma before "and" in this situation, and it was formerly considered wrong. Examples of lists include—"At the sports club we can play tennis, squash, badminton and table tennis," "We need to buy bread, milk, fruit, and sugar," and "They are studying French, German, Spanish and Russian." The individual items in a list can be quite long, as in "We opened the door, let ourselves in, fed the cat, and started to cook dinner" and "They consulted the map, planned the trip, got some foreign currency and left before we realized it." Confusion may arise if the last item in the list contains "and" in its own right, as in "The award categories include rock, pop, jazz, blues, folk and country and western." In this example a comma should be placed before the "and" after "folk."

In cases where there is a list of adjectives before a noun, the use of commas is now optional although it was formerly standard practice. Thus both "She wore a long, red, sequined dress" and "She wore a long red sequined dress" are used. When the adjective immediately before the noun has a closer relationship with it than the other adjectives no comma should be used, as in "a beautiful old Spanish village."

The comma is used to separate clauses or phrases that are parenthetical or naturally cut off from the rest of a sentence, as in "My mother, who was Irish, was very superstitious." In such a sentence the clause within the commas can be removed without altering the basic meaning. Care should be taken to include both commas. Commas are not normally used to separate main clauses and relative clauses, as in "The woman whom I met was my friend's sister." Nor are they usually used to separate main clauses and subordinate clauses, as in "He left when we arrived" and "They came to the party although we didn't expect them to." If the subordinate clause precedes the main clause, it is sometimes followed by a comma, especially if it is a reasonably long clause, as in "Although we stopped and thought about it, we still made the wrong decision." If the clause is quite short, or if it is a short phrase, a comma is not usually inserted, as in "Although it rained we had a good vacation" and "Although poor they were happy." The use of commas to separate such words and expression from the rest of the sentence to which they are related is optional. Thus it is possible to write "However, he could be right" or "However he could be right." The longer the expression is, the more likely it is to have a comma after it, as in "On the other hand, we may decide not to go."

Commas are always used to separate terms of address, interjections, or question tags from the rest of the sentence, as in "Please come this way, Ms Levy, and make yourself at home," "Hi, guys, what can I get you?" and "It's cold today, isn't it?"

Commas may be used to separate main clauses joined by a coordinating conjunction, but this is not usual if the clauses have the same subject or object, as in "She swept the floor and dusted the table." In cases where the subjects are different and the clauses are fairly long, it is best to insert a comma, as in "They took all the furniture with them, and she was left with nothing."

A comma can be inserted to avoid repeating a verb in the second of two clauses, as in "He plays golf and tennis, his brother basketball."

commands

These are expressed in the imperative mood, as in "Be quiet!", "Stop crying!", "Go away!"

common noun

Simply the name of an ordinary, everyday non-specific thing or person, as opposed to proper nouns, which refer to the names of particular individuals or specific places. Common nouns include "baby," "cat," "girl," "hat," "park," "chair," and "table."

comparison of adjectives

This is achieved in two different ways. Some adjectives form their comparative by adding -er to the positive or absolute form, as in "braver," "louder," "madder," "shorter," and "taller." Other adjectives form their comparative by using "more" in conjunction with them, as in "more beautiful," "more realistic," "more suitable," and "more tactful." Which is the correct form is largely a matter of length. One-syllable adjectives, such as "loud," add -er, as in "louder." Two-syllable adjectives sometimes have both forms as a possibility, as in "gentler/more gentle," and "cleverest/most clever." Adjectives with three or more syllables usually form their comparatives with "more," as in "more comfortable," "more generous," "more regular" and "more understanding." Some adjectives are irregular in their comparative forms, as in "good/better," "bad/worse," "many/more." Only if they begin with un- are they likely to end in -er, as in "untrustworthier."

Some adjectives by their very definitions do not normally have a comparative form, for example "unique."

complement

The equivalent of the OBJECT in a clause with a LINKING VERB. In the sentence "Jasmine is a doctor," "a doctor" is the complement. In the sentence "Jack is a good father," "a good father" is the complement," and in the sentence "Our son is an excellent football player," "an excellent football player" is the complement.

complex sentence

A type of sentence in which there is a MAIN CLAUSE and one or more subordinate clauses. The sentence "We went to visit him although he had been unfriendly to us" is a complex sentence since it is composed of a main clause and one subordinate clause ("although he had been unfriendly to us"). The sentence "We wondered where he had gone and why he was upset" is a complex sentence since it has a main clause and two subordinate clauses ("where he had gone" and "why he was upset").

compound sentence

A type of sentence with more than one clause and linked by a coordinating conjunction, such as "and" or "but," as in "He applied for a new position and got it" and "I went to the theater but I didn't enjoy the show."

concord *see* **number agreement**.

concrete noun

The name of something that can be touched, as opposed to an abstract noun, which cannot. Concrete nouns include "bag," "glass," "plate," "pot," "pants," "field," "yard," "flower," "potato," "foot," and "shoe." *See* ABSTRACT NOUN.

conjunction

A word that connects words, clauses, or sentences. Conjunctions are of two types. A **coordinating conjunction** joins units of equal status, as in "bread and butter," "We asked for some food and we got it." A **subordinating conjunction** joins a dependent or subordinating clause to main verbs: in "We asked him why he was there," "why he was there" is a subordinate clause and thus "why" is a subordinating conjunction.

content words *see* **function word**.

continuous tenses *see* **tense**.

contraction *see* **abbreviation**.

copula *see* **linking verb**.

copular verb *see* **equative** *and* **linking verb**.

count noun

A noun that can be preceded by "a" and can take a plural, as in "hat/hats," "flower/flowers." *See also* MASS NOUN.

D

dangling participle

A participle that has been misplaced in a sentence. A participle is often used to introduce a phrase that is attached to a subject mentioned later in a sentence, as in "Worn out by the long walk, she fell to the ground in a faint." "Worn out" is the participle and "she" the subject. Another example is "Laughing in glee at having won, she ordered some champagne." In this sentence "laughing" is the participle and "she" is the subject. It is a common error for such a participle not to be related to any subject, as in "Imprisoned in the dark basement, it seemed a long time since she had seen the sun." This participle is said to be "dangling." Another example of a dangling participle is contained in "Living alone, the days seemed long."

   It is also a common error for a participle to be related to the wrong subject in a sentence, as in "Painting the ceiling, some of the plaster fell on his head," "Painting" is the participle and should go with a subject "he." Instead it goes with "some of the plaster." Participles in this situation are more correctly known as **misrelated participles**, although they are also called dangling participles.

dash

A punctuation mark in the form of a short line that indicates a short break in the continuity of a sentence, as in "He has never been any trouble at school—quite the reverse," "I was amazed when he turned up—I thought he was still overseas." In such situations it serves the same purpose as parentheses, except that it is frequently considered more informal. The dash should be used sparingly. Depending on it too much can lead to careless writing with ideas set down at random rather than turned into a piece of coherent prose.

The dash can be used to emphasize a word or phrase, as in "They said goodbye then—forever." It can also be used to add a remark to the end of a sentence, as in "They had absolutely no money—a regular state of affairs toward the end of the month." The dash can also be used to introduce a statement that amplifies or explains what has been said, as in "The burglars took everything of value—her jewelry, the TV set, the DVD player, the hi-fi system, and several thousand dollars." It can be used to summarize what has gone before, as in "Disease, poverty, ignorance—these are the problems facing us."

The dash is also used to introduce an afterthought, as in "You can come with me—but you might not want to." It can also introduce a sharp change of subject, as in "I'm just making coffee— what was that noise?" It can also be used to introduce some kind of balance in a sentence, as in "It's going to take two of us to get this table out of here—one to move it and one to hold the door open."

The dash is sometimes found in pairs. A pair of dashes acts in much the same way as a set of parentheses. A pair of dashes can be used to indicate a break in a sentence, as in "We prayed—prayed as we had never prayed before—that the kids would be safe," "It was—on reflection—his best performance yet," and "He introduced me to his wife—a charming attractive woman—before he left."

Dashes are used to indicate hesitant speech, as in "I don't— well—maybe—you could be right." They can be used to indicate the omission of part of a word or name, as in "Stupidity really p—es me off," "He's having an affair with Mrs D—." They can also be used (in a form known as an *en* dash) between points in time or space, as in "Philadelphia–Washington" and "1750–1790."

dates

These are usually written in figures, as in 1999, rather than in words, as in nineteen ninety-nine, except in formal contexts, such as legal documents. There are various ways of writing dates. The standard form in North America is "February 24, 1970," and that is a possibility in Britain also. Alternately, some people write "24 February 1970" or "24th February 1970." Care should be taken with the writing of dates entirely in numbers, especially if one is corresponding with someone in Britain. In North America the month is put first, followed by the day of the month, and the year, as in "2/3/50," or "February 3 1950." In Britain the day of the month is put first, the month second, and the year third. Thus in Britain "2/3/50" would be "2 March 1950."

Centuries may be written either in figures, as in "the 19th century," or in words, as in "the nineteenth century."

Decades and centuries are now usually written without apostrophes, as in "1980s" and "1990s."

dative case

The case that indicates "to" or "for." This is applicable to Latin but not to English, where such meanings are expressed by prepositional phrases. In English the INDIRECT OBJECT is equivalent to the dative case in some situations.

deca-

A prefix derived from Greek meaning "ten," as in decade, decathlon, decameter.

deci-

A prefix derived from Latin meaning "tenth," as in decibel, decimal, decimate, deciliter.

declarative sentence

A sentence that conveys information. The subject precedes the verb in it. Examples include "They won the battle," "He has moved to another neighborhood," "Lots of people go there," and "There is a new person in charge."

declarative mood *see* indicative mood.

declension

The variation of the form of a noun, adjective, or pronoun to show different cases, such as nominative and accusative. It also refers to the class into which such words are placed, as in first declension, second declension, etc. The term applies to languages such as Latin but is not applicable to English.

definite article

A term for "the," which is the most frequently used word in the English language. "The" is used to refer back to a person or thing that has already been mentioned, as in "Jack and Jill built a model.

The model was of a ship" and "We've bought a car. It was the cheapest car we could find."

"The" can be used to make a general statement about all things of a particular type, as in "The computer has led to the loss of many jobs" and "The car has caused damage to the environment." "The" can be used to refer to a whole class or group, as in "the Italians," "the Kennedys," and "the younger generation."

"The" can also be used to refer to services or systems, as in "We are on the Internet" and "She prefers traveling by the subway." It can be used to refer to the name of a musical instrument when someone's ability to play it is being referred to, as in "Her son is learning to play the violin."

"The" indicates a person or thing to be the only one, as in the Torah, the King of Spain, the Empire State Building, the Taj Mahal, and the President of the United States.

"The" can be used instead of a possessive determiner to refer to parts of the body, as in "She took him by the arm" and "The dog bit him on the leg."

"The" is used in front of superlative adjectives, as in "the largest amount of money" and "the most beautiful baby." It can also be used to indicate that a person or thing is unique or exceptional, as in "the political debater of his generation." In this last sense "the" is pronounced "thee."

degree

A level of comparison of gradable adjectives. The degrees of comparison comprise **absolute** or **positive**, as in "big," "calm," "dark," "fair," "hot," "late," "short," and "tall"; **comparative**, as in "bigger," "calmer," "darker," "fairer," "hotter," "later," "shorter," and "taller"; **superlative**, as in "biggest," "calmest," "darkest," "fairest," "hottest," "latest," "shortest" and "tallest."

Degree can also refer to adverbs. Adverbs of degree include "extremely," "very," "greatly," "rather," "really," "remarkably," "terribly," as in "an extremely rare case," "a very old man," "He's remarkably brave," and "We're terribly pleased."

demi-

A prefix derived from Old French meaning "half," as in demi-god, demi-veg.

demonstrative determiner

A determiner that is used to indicate things or people in relationship to the speaker or writer in space or time. "This" and "these" indicate nearness to the speaker, as in "Will you take this book home?" and "These flowers are for you." "That" and "those" indicate distance from the speaker, as in "Get that creature out of here!" and "Aren't those flowers over there beautiful!"

demonstrative pronoun

A pronoun that is similar to a DEMONSTRATIVE DETERMINDER except that it stands alone in place of a noun rather than preceding a noun, as in "I'd like to give you this," "What is that?", "These are interesting books," and "Those are not his shoes."

dependent clause

A clause that cannot stand alone and make sense, unlike an independent or MAIN CLAUSE. Dependent clauses depend on the main clause. The term is the same as SUBORDINATE CLAUSE.

derivation

(1) The etymology of a word, as in "The derivation of the expression is unknown."
(2) The process of forming a new word by adding an AFFIX of some kind to an existing word or base, as in "helpless" from "help" and "maker" from "make."

derivative

A word that is formed by DERIVATION. For example, "sweetly" is a derivative of "sweet," "peaceful" is a derivative from "peace," "clinging" is derived from "cling" and "shortest" is derived from "short."

derm-

A prefix derived from Greek meaning "skin," as in dermatitis, dermatologist, dermatology.

determiner

A word that is used in front of a noun or pronoun to tell us something about it. Unlike an ADJECTIVE, it does not, strictly speaking, "describe" a noun or pronoun. Determiners are divided into the following categories: **articles** (a, an, the) as in "a cat," "an eagle," "the book"; **demonstrative determiners** (this, that, these, those) as in "this girl," "that boy," "those people"; **possessive determiners** (my, your, his/her/its, our, their) as in "my dog," "her house," "its color," "their responsibility"; **numbers** (one, two, three, four, etc., first, second, third, fourth, etc.) as in "two reasons," "five ways," "ten children"; and **indefinite** or **general determiners** (all, another, any, both, each, either, enough, every, few, fewer, less, little, many, most, much, neither, no, other, several, some) as in "both parents," "enough food," "several issues." Many words used as determiners are also pronouns. *See* ADJECTIVE; DEMONSTRATIVE DETERMINER; POSSESSIVE DETERMINER; NUMBERS; INDEFINITE DETERMINER.

di-

A prefix derived from Greek meaning "two" or "double," as in dioxide, dilemma, diphthong, disyllabic.

dia-

A prefix meaning "through," as in diaphanous; "apart," as in diacritical, diaphragm, dialysis; and "across," as in diameter.

diacritic

A mark placed over, under or through a letter to indicate a sound or stress value different from that of the same letter when it is unmarked. Diacritics include the cedilla, as in "façade," the German umlaut, as in "Mädchen," and dieresis, as in "naïve."

dialect

A variety of language that is distinct from other varieties in terms of pronunciation, accent, vocabulary, grammar, and sentence structure. The term "dialect" tends to imply a deviation from some standard form of language, usually the dialect used by educated people, known in English as "standard" English.

Dialects may be regional in nature. Thus in Britain there is a Cornish dialect, a Liverpool dialect, a Glasgow dialect, and so on. Alternately, they may be based on class differences, when they are sometimes known as "social dialects." These include working-class dialect, upper-class dialect, and so on.

dialog

The conversation in novels, etc., which is placed on a new line, often in a new paragraph, if there is a change of speaker, as in:

"We're going now," said Leo. "Do you want to join us? If you do you'd better hurry. We can't wait."

"Just go on," replied Ellen. "I'm not quite ready. I'll catch you up."

diction

(1) The choice of words in writing or speech, especially with regard to correctness, clarity, or effectiveness, as in "The content of his paper was very interesting but his diction was poor."
(2) The pronunciation and enunciation of words in speaking and singing, as in "She has a beautiful natural singing voice but should take lessons in diction."

dieresis

A mark that is placed over a vowel to indicate that it is sounded separately from a neighboring vowel, as in "naïve," "Chloë."

digraph

A group of two letters representing one sound, as in "ay" in "hay," "ey" in "key," "oy" in "boy," "ph" in "phone," and "th" in "thin." When the digraph consists of two letters physically joined together, as "æ," it is called a "ligature."

diminutive

Something small or a small form or version of something, as in "booklet," "droplet," "auntie," "doggy," "islet," "piglet," "poppet," "snippet," "starlet," "kitchenette," "hillock," "paddock," "manni-kin," "lambkin," "duckling," "gosling," "nestling," "majorette," "pipette." Proper names often have diminutive forms, as in Andy for Andrew, Annie for Anne, Babs for Barbara, Bill for William, Charlie for Charles, Jackie for Jacqueline, Jimmy for James, Lizzie for Elizabeth, Meg for Margaret, Nell for Helen, Pat for Patrick, and Teddy for Edward.

diphthong

A speech sound that changes its quality within the same single syllable. The sound begins as for one vowel and moves on as for another. Since the sound glides from one vowel into another, a diphthong is sometimes called a **gliding vowel**. Examples include the vowels sounds in "rain," "weigh," "either," "voice," "height," "aisle," "road," "soul," "know," "house," "care," "pure," "during," "here," and "weird."

direct object

The noun, noun phrase, noun or nominal clause, or pronoun that is acted upon by the action of a transitive verb. In the sentence "She bought milk," "bought" is a transitive verb and "milk" is a noun which is the direct object. In the sentence "She bought loads of clothes," "bought" is a transitive verb and "loads of clothes" is the direct object. In the sentence "He knows what happened," "knows" is a transitive verb and "what happened" is a "noun clause" or "nominal clause." A direct object is frequently known just as object. *See* INDIRECT OBJECT.

direct speech

The reporting of speech by repeating exactly the actual words used by the speaker. In the sentence "Al said, 'I am tired of this,'" "I am tired of this" is a piece of direct speech because it represents exactly what Al said. Similarly, in the sentence "Teresa asked, 'Where are you going?'" "Where are you going?" is a piece of direct speech since it represents exactly what Teresa said.

QUOTATION MARKS are used at the beginning and end of pieces of direct speech. Only the words actually spoken are placed within the quotation marks, as in

"If I were you," he said, "I would refuse to go."

The quotation marks involved can be either single or double, according to preference or house style.

If there is a statement such as "he said" following the piece of direct speech, a comma is placed before the second inverted comma, as in

"Come along," he said.

If the piece of direct speech is a question or exclamation, a question mark or exclamation point is placed before the second inverted comma, as in

"What are you doing?" asked Jamal.

   and

"Get away from me!" she screamed.

If a statement such as "he said" interrupts a sentence in direct speech, a comma is placed after "he said" and the second part of direct speech does not begin with a capital letter, as in

"I know very well," he said, "that you do not like me."

Note that the period at the end of a piece of direct speech should go before the closing inverted comma.

If the piece of direct speech quoted takes up more than one paragraph, quotation marks are placed at the beginning of each new paragraph. However, quotation marks are not placed at the end of each paragraph, just at the end of the final one.

When writing a story, etc., that includes dialog or conversation, each new piece of direct speech should begin on a new line or sometimes in a new paragraph.

Quotation marks are not used only to indicate direct speech. Sometimes they are used to indicate the title of a book or newspaper. The quotation marks used in this way can be either single or double. If a piece of direct speech contains the title of a book, newspaper, etc., it should be put in the opposite quotation marks to those used to enclose the piece of direct speech. Thus, if single quotation marks have been used for the direct speech, then double quotation marks should be used for the title, as in

'Have you read "Animal Farm" by George Orwell?' the teacher asked.

If double quotation marks have been used for the direct speech, single quotation marks should be used for the title, as in

"Have you read 'Animal Farm' by George Orwell?" the teacher asked.

Sometimes titles are put in italic type instead of quotation marks. This avoids the clumsiness that can occur when both sets of quotation marks end on the same word, as in

The student replied, 'No, I have not read *Animal Farm*.'

dis-

A prefix derived from Latin meaning "opposite," "not," as in disappear, disapprove, disband, disbelieve, disclaim, disconnect, discontinue, disenchant, disengage, disinherit, dislike, disobey, dispossess, distrust, disunite.

distributive pronoun

A pronoun that refers to individual members of a class or group. These include "each," "either," "neither," "none," "everyone," "no one." Such pronouns, where relevant, should be accompanied by singular verbs and singular personal pronouns, as in "All the men are to be considered for the new positions. Each is to send in his application." Problems arise when the sex of the noun to which the distributive pronoun refers back is either unknown or unspecified. Formerly it was the convention to treat such nouns as masculine and so to make the distributive pronoun masculine, as in "All students must obey the rules. Each is to provide his own sports equipment." Nowadays this convention is frequently considered to be unacceptably sexist and attempts have been made to get around this. One solution is to use "him/her" (or "him or her"), etc., as in "The students have received a directive from the professor. Each is to produce his/her paper by tomorrow." This convention is considered by many people to be clumsy. They prefer to be ungrammatical and use a plural personal pronoun, as in "The students are being punished. Each is to inform their parents." Where possible it is preferable to rephrase sentences to avoid being either sexist or ungrammatical, as in "All the students must tell their parents."

Each, either, etc., in such contexts is fairly formal. In less formal situations "each of," "either of," etc., is more usual, as in "Each of the boys will have to train really hard to win" and "Either of the dresses is perfectly suitable."

disyllabic

A term that describes a word with two syllables. For example, "window" is disyllabic, since it consists of the syllable "win" and the syllable "dow." Similarly "curtain" is disyllabic since it consists of the syllable "cur" and the syllable "tain."

do

An auxiliary verb that is used to form negative forms, as in, "I do not agree with you," "They do not always win," "He does not wish to go," and "She did not approve of their behavior." It is also used to form interrogative forms, as in "Do you agree?", "Does she know about it?", "Did you see that?", and "I prefer to go by train.

Don't you?" Do is also used for emphasis, as in "I do believe you're right" and "They do know, don't they?"

-dom

A suffix meaning "state, condition," as in boredom, freedom, officialdom, martyrdom. It can also mean "rank or status," as in earldom, dukedom, or "domain or territory," as in kingdom.

double negative

The occurrence of two negative words in a single sentence or clause, as in "He didn't say nothing" and "We never had no quarrel." This is usually considered incorrect in standard English, although it is a feature of some social or regional dialects. The use of the double negative, if taken literally, often has the opposite meaning to the one intended. Thus "He didn't say nothing" conveys the idea that "He said something."

Some double negatives are considered acceptable, as in "I wouldn't be surprised if they don't turn up," although it is better to restrict such constructions to informal contexts. The sentence quoted conveys the impression that the speaker will be quite surprised if "they" do "turn up." Another example of an acceptable double negative is "I can't not worry about the children. Anything could have happened to them." Again this type of construction is best restricted to informal contexts.

It is the semi-negative forms, such as "hardly" and "scarcely," that cause most problems with regard to double negatives, as in "We didn't have hardly any money to buy food" and "They didn't have barely enough time to catch the bus." Such sentences are incorrect.

double passive

A clause that contains two verbs in the passive, the second of which is an infinitive, as in "The goods are expected to be dispatched some time this week." Some examples of double passives are clumsy or ungrammatical and should be avoided, as in "Redundancy notices are proposed to be issued next week."

doubles

Words that habitually go together, as in "out and out," "neck and neck," "over and over," "hale and hearty," "rant and rave," "fast and furious," "hue and cry," "stuff and nonsense," "rough and ready," "might and main," "give and take," "ups and downs," "fair and square," "high and dry," and "wear and tear." Doubles are also sometimes called **dyads**.

doublets

Pairs of words that have developed from the same original word but now differ somewhat in form and usually in meaning. Examples include "human" and "humane," "shade" and "shadow," "hostel" and "hotel," "frail" and "fragile," and "fashion" and "faction."

doubling of consonants

These can cause spelling problems. There are a few rules that help to solve these problems. These include the following: in words of one syllable ending in a single consonant preceded by a single vowel, the consonant is doubled when an ending starting with a vowel is added, as in "drop" and "dropped," "pat" and "patting," and "rub" and "rubbing."

In words of more than one syllable that end in a single consonant preceded by a single vowel, the consonant is doubled if the stress is on the last syllable, as in "begin" and "beginning," "occur" and "occurring," "prefer" and "preferred," "refer" and "referring" and "commit," and "committed." In similar words where the stress is not on the last syllable, the consonant does not double, as in "bigot" and "bigoted" and "develop" and "developed."

dramatic irony

A situation in which a character in a play, novel, etc., says or does something that has a meaning for the audience or reader, other than the obvious meaning, that he/she does not understand. Its use is common in both comedy and tragedy.

dual gender

A category of nouns in which there is no indication of gender. The nouns referred to include a range of words used for people, and occasionally animals, which can be of either gender. Unless the gender is specified we do not know the sex of the person or animal referred to. Such words include "artist," "author," "poet," "singer," "child," "student," "baby," "parent," "teacher," "dog." Such words give rise to problems with accompanying singular pronouns. *See* EACH.

dummy subject

A SUBJECT that has no intrinsic meaning but is inserted to maintain a balanced grammatical structure. In the sentences "It has started to rain" and "It is nearly midnight," "it" is a dummy subject. In the sentences "There is nothing else to say" and "There is no reason for his behavior," "there" is a dummy subject.

dyads *see* doubles.

dynamic verb

A verb with a meaning that indicates action, as "work" in "They work hard," "play" in "The boys play football at the weekend" and "come" in "The girls come here every Sunday."

dys-

A prefix derived from Greek meaning "bad," as in dysfunctional, dyslexia, dysmenorrhea, dyspepsia.

E

each

A word that can be either a DETERMINER or a DISTRIBUTIVE PRONOUN. Each as a determiner is used before a singular noun and is accompanied by a singular verb, as in "Each candidate is to reapply," "Each athlete has a place in the final," "Each country is represented by a head of state," and "Each chair was covered in chintz."

Each of can sometimes be used instead of each, as in "each of the candidates." Again a singular verb is used, as in "Each of the books has pages missing," "Each of the chairs has a broken leg," and "Each of the students is to make a contribution to the cost of the outing." Each of can also be used in front of plural pronouns, as in "each of them." Once again a singular verb is used, as in "Each of them wants something different," "Each of us is supposed to make a contribution," and "Each of the words has several meanings." If the user wishes to emphasize the fact that something is true about every member of a group, **each one of** should be used and not "every," as in "Each one of them feels guilty," "Each one of us has a part to play," and "Each one of the actors has improved."

As a pronoun, each also takes a singular verb, as in "They hate each other. Each is plotting revenge," "These exercises are not a waste of time. Each provides valuable experience." For emphasis **each one** can be used, as in "We cannot leave any of these books behind. Each one of them is necessary," and "We should not dismiss any of the staff. Each one has a part to play in the new firm."

Each, where relevant, should be accompanied by a singular personal pronoun, as in "Each girl has to provide her own sports equipment," "Each of the men is to take a turn at working night shift," "The boys are all well off and each can afford the cost of the vacation," and "There are to be no exceptions among the female staff. Each one has to work full time."

Problems arise when the noun that each refers back to is of unknown or unspecified sex. Formerly nouns in such situations were assumed to be masculine, as in "Each student was required to bring his own tennis racket" and "Each of the students has to provide himself with a tape recorder." Nowadays such a convention is regarded as being sexist and the use of "he/she," "his/her," etc., is proposed, as in "Each student was required to bring his/her (or "his or her") own tennis racket" and "Each student has to provide himself/herself (or "himself or herself") with a tape recorder." Even in written English such a convention can be clumsy and it is even more so in spoken English. For this reason many people decide to be ungrammatical and opt for "Each student was required to bring their own tennis racket" and "Each student has to provide themselves with a tape recorder."

Both sexism and grammatical error can be avoided by rephrasing such sentences, as in "All students are required to bring their own tennis rackets" and "All students have to provide themselves with tape recorders."

Each is used rather than every when the user is thinking of the members of a group as individuals.

eco-

A prefix indicating ecology. Following the increased awareness of the importance of the environment, there has been a growing interest in ecology and many words beginning with eco- have been added to the English language. Some of these are scientific terms such as ecotype, ecosystem, ecospecies. Others are more general terms, such as ecocatastrophe, ecopolitics, ecotourism, and some are even slang terms, such as ecofreak and econut.

-ectomy

A suffix of Greek origin that indicates "surgical removal," as in hysterectomy (the surgical removal of the womb), mastectomy (the surgical removal of a breast), and appendectomy (the surgical removal of the appendix).

-ed

A suffix that forms the past tense and past participles of regular verbs, as in "asked," "blinded," "caused," "darkened," "escaped," "frightened," "guarded," "hunted," "injured," "jilted," "kicked," "landed," "marked," "noted," "opened," "painted," "quarreled," "rattled," "started," "tormented," "unveiled," "washed," "yielded," "zoned." Some past participles ending in "-ed" can act as adjectives, as in "darkened room," "escaped prisoners," "frightened children," "hunted animals," "painted faces," and "tormented souls."

In the case of some verbs, the past tense and past participle may end in "-ed" or "t," according to preference. Such verbs include "burn," "dream," "dwell," "kneel," "lean," "leap," "smell," "spell," "spill," and "spoil." Thus "burned" and "burnt," "dreamed" and "dreamt," "kneeled" and "knelt," and "leaned" and "leant," etc., are acceptable forms.

-ee

A suffix that is derived from French and is used as part of nouns that are the recipients of an action, as in deportee (a person who has been deported); employee (a person who is employed); interviewee (a person who is being interviewed); licensee (a person who has been licensed); trainee (a person who is being trained).

The suffix -ee can also be used as part of a noun indicating a person who acts or behaves in a particular way, as in absentee (a person who absents himself/herself) and escapee (a person who escapes).

e.g.

The abbreviation of the Latin phrase *exempli gratia*, which means "for example." It is used before examples of what has previously been referred to, as in "The tourists want to visit the historic sites of Philadelphia, e.g. Independence Hall and the Liberty Bell." By its very nature, e.g. is mostly restricted to written English, becoming "for example" in speech. Many writers also prefer to use "for example" rather than e.g. The abbreviation is usually preceded by a comma and both letters usually have a period after them, as e.g.

either

A word that can be used as either a determiner or a distributive pronoun. As a determiner it is used with a singular verb, as in "Either hotel is expensive" and "In principle, they are both against the plan but is either likely to vote for it?"

Either of can be used instead of either. It is used before a plural noun, as in "either of the applicants" and "either of the houses." It is accompanied by a singular verb, as in "Either of the applicants is suitable" and "Either of the houses is big enough for their family."

Either can be used as a distributive pronoun and takes a singular verb, as in "We have looked at both houses and either is suitable" and "She cannot decide between the two dresses but either is appropriate for the occasion." This use is rather formal.

In the **either . . . or** construction, a singular verb is used if both subjects are singular, as in "Either Claudia or Judy knows what to do" and "Either my mother or my father plans to be present." A plural verb is used if both nouns involved are plural, as in "Either men or women can play" and "Either houses or apartments are available."

When a combination of singular and plural subjects is involved, the verb traditionally agrees with the subject that is nearer to it, as in "Either his parents or his sister is going to come" and "Either his grandmother or his parents are going to come."

As a pronoun, either should be used only of two possibilities.

electro-

A prefix meaning "electric, electrical" as in electrocardiograph, electromagnetic, electroscope, electrotherapy.

elision

The omission of a speech sound or syllable, as in the omission of "d" in one of the possible pronunciations of "Wednesday" and in the omission of "ce" from the pronunciation of "Gloucester."

ellipsis

An omission of some kind. It can refer to the omission of words from a statement because they are thought to be obvious from the context. In many cases it involves using an auxiliary verb on its own rather than a full verb, as in "Debbie won't accept it but Gina will" and "They would go if they could." In such cases the full form of "Debbie won't accept it but Gina will accept it" and "They would go if they could go" would sound unnatural and repetitive. This is common in spoken English.

Some sentences containing an ellipsis sound clumsy as well as ungrammatical, as in "This is as good, or perhaps even better than that," where "as" is omitted after "good" and in "People have and still do express their disapproval about it," where "expressed" is omitted after "have." Care should be taken to avoid ellipsis if the use of it is going to be ambiguous or clumsy.

Ellipsis is often used to indicate an omission from a quoted passage. If part of a passage is quoted and there is a gap before the next piece of the same passage is required to be quoted, an ellipsis is used in the form of three dots (. . .). If the part of the passage quoted does not start at the beginning of a sentence the ellipsis precedes it.

emphasizing adjective

An adjective that is used for emphasis. "Very" is an emphasizing adjective in the sentence "His very mother dislikes him" and "own" is an emphasizing adjective in "He likes to think that he is his own master."

emphasizing adverb

An adverb used for emphasis. "Really" is an emphasizing adverb in the sentence "She really doesn't care whether she lives or dies," and "positively" is an emphasizing adverb in the sentence "He positively does not want to know anything about it."

emphatic pronoun

A reflexive pronoun that is used for emphasis, as in "He knows himself that he is wrong," "She admitted herself that she had made a mistake" and "The teachers themselves say that the principal is too strict."

en-

A prefix meaning "causing to be," as in enrich, enlarge, and "putting into," as in endanger, enrage, enslave.

-en

A suffix with several functions. In one sense it means "causing to be," as in broaden, darken, gladden, lighten, sweeten. It also means a diminutive or small version of something, as in chicken, maiden. It also indicates what something is made of, as in silken, wooden, woolen. It is also used to form the past participle of many irregular verbs, as in broken, fallen, forgotten, taken.

ending

The final part of a word consisting of an inflection that is added to a BASE or root word. The "-ren" part of "children" is an ending, the "-er" of "poorer" is an ending and the "-ing" of "falling" is an ending.

epic

A word that originally referred to a very long narrative poem dealing with heroic deeds and adventures on a grand scale, as Homer's *Iliad*. In modern usage it has been extended to include novels or movies with some of these qualities.

epigram

A figure of speech consisting of a brief, pointed and witty saying, as in Jonathan Swift's "Every man desires to live long; but no man would be old" and Oscar Wilde's "A cynic is a man who knows the price of everything and the value of nothing." "Epigram" originally referred to a short poem inscribed on a public monument or tomb.

epithet

An adjective that describes a quality of a noun, as in "a beautiful dress," "an amazing story," "an enjoyable occasion." It is also used to indicate a term of abuse, as in "The drunk man let out a stream of epithets at the police officer."

eponym

A person after whom something is named. The name of the thing in question can also be referred to as an eponym, or it can be said to be **eponymous**, eponymous being the adjective from eponym. English has several eponymous words. Some of these are listed below together with their derivations:

Bailey bridge, a type of temporary military bridge that can be assembled very quickly, called after Sir Donald **Bailey** (1901–85), the British engineer who invented it.

Bowie knife, a type of hunting knife with a long curving blade, called after the American soldier and adventurer, James **Bowie** (1799–1836), who made it popular.

cardigan, a knitted jacket fastened with buttons called after the Earl of **Cardigan** (1797–1868) who was fond of wearing such a garment and was the British cavalry officer who led the unsuccessful Charge of the Light Brigade during the Crimean War (1854).

Celsius the temperature scale, called after the Swedish astronomer, Anders **Celsius** (1701–44).

freesia, a type of sweet-smelling flower, called after the German physician, Friedrich Heinrich Theodor **Freese** (died 1876).

greengage, a type of greenish plum, called after Sir William **Gage** (1777–1864), who introduced it into Britain from France.

leotard, a one-piece, close-fitting garment worn by acrobats and dancers, called after the French acrobat, Jules **Léotard** (1842–70), who introduced the costume as a circus garment.

praline, a type of confectionery made from nuts and sugar, called after Count Plessis-**Praslin** (1598–1675), a French field marshal, whose chef is said to have been the first person to make the sweet.

Plimsoll mark, any of a set of markings on the side of a ship that indicate the levels to which the ship may be safely loaded, called after Samuel **Plimsoll** (1824–98), a British merchant and shipping reformer.

salmonella, the bacteria that causes some diseases such as food poisoning, called after Daniel Elmer **Salmon** (1850–1914), the American veterinarian who identified it.

sandwich, a snack consisting of two pieces of buttered bread with a filling, called after the Earl of **Sandwich** (1718–92), who was such a compulsive gambler that he would not leave the gaming tables to eat, but had some cold beef between two slices of bread brought to him.

saxophone, a type of keyed brass instrument often used in jazz music, called after Adolphe **Sax** (1814–94), the Belgiaan instrument-maker who invented it.

shrapnel, an explosive projectile that contains bullets or fragments of metal and a charge that is exploded before impact, called after the British army officer, Henry **Shrapnel** (1761–1842), who invented it.

stetson, a type of wide-brimmed high-crowned felt hat, called after its designer, the American hat-maker, John Batterson **Stetson** (1830–1906).

trilby, a type of soft felt hat with an indented crown, called after "**Trilby**," the dramatized version of the novel by the British writer, George du Maurier. The heroine of the play, Trilby O' Ferrall, wore such a hat.

wellington, a waterproof rubber boot that extends to the knee, called after the Duke of **Wellington** (1769–1852), who defeated Napoleon at Waterloo (1815).

equative

A term that indicates that one thing is equal to, or the same as, another. The verb "to be" is sometimes known as an **equative verb** because it links a subject and complement that are equal to each other, as in "He is a rogue" ("he" and "rogue" refer to the same person) and "My sister is a journalist" ("my sister" and "journalist" refer to the same person). Other equative verbs include "appear," "become," "look," "remain," and "seem," as in "He looks a nasty person" and "She became a rich woman." Such verbs are more usually known as **copular verbs**.

-er

A suffix with several functions. It can indicate "a person who does something," as in bearer, cleaner, employer, farmer, manager. Some words in this category can also end in "-or," as in adviser/advisor. It can also indicate "a person who is engaged in something," as in lawyer. It also indicates "a thing that does something," as in blender, cooker, mower, printer, strainer. It can also indicate the comparative form of an adjective, as in darker, fairer, older, shorter, younger. It can also indicate "someone that comes from somewhere," as in New Yorker.

-ese

A suffix meaning "belonging to, coming from" and is used of people and languages, as Chinese, Japanese, Portuguese. By extension it refers to words indicating some kind of jargon, as computerese, journalese, officialese.

Esq.

A word that can be used (mostly in formal contexts) instead of "Mr" when addressing an envelope to a man, as in "Ross Petersen, Esq." instead of "Mr Ross Petersen." It is usually spelt with a period and with a comma in front of it.

-esque

A suffix of French origin that means "in the style or fashion of," as in Junoesque, statuesque, Picassoesque, Ramboesque.

-ess

A suffix that was formerly widely used to indicate the feminine form of a word, as authoress from "author," poetess from "poet," editress from "editor," sculptress from "sculptor." In many cases the supposed male form, such as "author," is now considered a neutral form and so is used of both a woman and a man. Thus a woman as well as a man may be an author, a poet, an editor, a sculptor, etc. Some words ending in -ess remain, as princess, duchess, heiress, hostess. Actress and waitress are still also fairly widespread.

-est

A suffix that indicates the superlative forms of adjectives, as in biggest, hardest, lowest, smallest, ugliest.

etc.

The abbreviation of a Latin phrase *et cetera*, meaning "and the rest, and other things." It is used at the end of lists to indicate that there exist other examples of the kind of thing that has just been named, as in "He grows potatoes, carrots, turnips, etc.," "The girls can play tennis, volleyball, squash, etc.," "The main branch of the bank can supply francs, marks, lire, kroner, etc." Etc. is preceded by a comma and is usually spelt with a period.

-ette

A suffix indicating a diminutive or smaller version, as cigarette, kitchenette, rosette. It can also indicate "imitation," as in flannel-ette, leatherette, satinette. It can also indicate "female," as in majorette, usherette, suffragette. In this last sense it has some-times been used disparagingly, as in farmerette (a derogatory word for a female farmer) and sailorette (a derogatory word for a female sailor).

etymology

The source of the formation of a word and the development of its meaning, as in "What is the etymology of the word 'biochemistry'?" It also means the branch of language studies that deals with the origin and development of words, as in "He specializes in etymology." In addition it refers to an account or statement of the formation of a word or phrase, as in "Does that dictionary have etymologies?" In larger dictionaries it is usual to include etymologies, often at the end of each entry. These indicate which language the relevant word has been derived from, for example, whether it has come from Old English, Norse, Latin, Greek, French, German, Dutch, Italian, Spanish, a Native American language, etc. Alternately they indicate which person, place, etc., the word has been named after. Some dictionaries also include the date at which the relevant word entered the English language. *See* BORROWING.

Many words and phrases in the English language are of unknown or uncertain origin. In such cases much guesswork goes on and various suggestions are put forward, most of which cannot be proved.

euphemism

A term given to an expression that is a milder, more pleasant, less direct way of saying something that might be thought to be too harsh or direct. English has a great many euphemisms, many of these referring to certain areas of life. Euphemisms range from the high-flown to the coy to slang. Some examples of euphemisms and of the areas in which they tend to occur are listed below:

euphemisms for "die" or "be dead": be in the arms of Jesus, be laid to rest, be with one's maker, be no longer with us, be with the Lord, be written out of the script, bite the dust, buy the farm, cash in one's chips, croak, depart this life, go to a better place, go the way of all flesh, go to one's long home, go to the happy hunting grounds, have been taken by the grim reaper, have bought it, have breathed one's last, have gone to a better place, kick the bucket, meet one's end, pass away, pay the supreme sacrifice, pop off, push up the daisies, rest in peace, shuffle off this mortal coil, slip one's rope, turn up one's toes.

euphemisms for "old": getting on a bit, not as young as one was, not in the first flush of youth, in the sunset years, in the twilight years, of advanced years, so many years young (as in "90 years young").

euphemisms for "suicide": do away with oneself, die by one's own hand, end it all, fall on one's sword, make away with oneself, take one's own life, take the easy way out.

euphemisms for "to dismiss": declare (someone) redundant, deselect, dispense with (someone's) services, give early retirement to, give (someone) a golden handshake, give (someone) his/her marching orders, let (someone) go, not renew (someone's) contract.

euphemisms for "drunk": blotto, feeling no pain, happy, in one's cups, legless, merry, one over the eight, plastered, three sheets in the wind, tiddly, tipsy, tired and emotional, well-oiled.

euphemisms for "naked": in a state of nature, in one's birthday suit, in the buff, in the raw, starkers, without a stitch, wearing only a smile.

euphemisms for "pregnant": awaiting the patter of tiny feet, expecting, expecting a happy event, in a delicate condition, in the club, in the family way, in the pudding club, with a bun in the oven.

euphemisms for "to have sexual intercourse": be intimate with, do it, get one's end away, go to bed with, have it off with, make love, make out, sleep with, score.

euphemisms for "sexual intercourse": hanky-panky, intimacy, roll in the hay.

euphemisms for "to go to the bathroom": answer the call of nature, freshen up, go somewhere, go to the little girls' (or boys') room, pay a visit, powder one's nose, spend a penny, take a slash, wash one's hands.

euphemisms for "bathroom": can, john, powder room, rest room, the facilities, the conveniences, the little girl's room/the little boys' room, the smallest room, the plumbing, wash room.

euphemisms and political correctness: many of the expressions advocated by the politically correct movement for viewing physical and mental disabilities in a more positive light are in fact euphemisms. These include "aurally challenged" for "deaf," "optically challenged" for "blind," and "differently abled" for "physically disabled."

Euro-

A prefix meaning either "referring to Europe," or, more commonly now "referring to the European Union," as in Euro-MP, Eurocrat, Eurocurrency.

every

A word used with a singular noun to indicate that all the members of a group are being referred to. It takes a singular verb, as in "Every soldier must report for duty," "Every machine is to be inspected," "Every house has a different view." Every should also be accompanied, where relevant, by a singular pronoun, as in "Every boy has his job to do," "Every girl is to wear a dress," "Every machine is to be replaced." Problems arise when the sex of the noun to which every refers is unknown or unspecified. Formerly it was the custom to assume such a noun to be masculine and to use masculine pronouns, as in "Every student is to behave himself properly." This assumption is now regarded as sexist, and to avoid this "he/she," "him/her" and "his/her" can be used. Many people feel that this convention can become clumsy and prefer to be ungrammatical by using "they," "them," and "their," as in "Every student is to behave themselves properly." Many sentences of this kind can be rephrased to avoid being either sexist or ungrammatical, as in "All students are to behave themselves properly." *See* EACH.

everyone

A pronoun that takes a singular verb, as in "Everyone is welcome" and "Everyone has the right to a decent standard of living." In order to be grammatically correct, it should be accompanied, where relevant, by a singular personal pronoun but it is subject to the same kind of treatment as EVERY.

ex-

A prefix meaning "former," as in ex-chairman, ex-president, ex-wife.

exclamation

A word, phrase, or sentence called out with strong feeling of some kind. It is marked by an **exclamation point**, which occurs at the end of the exclamation, as in "Get lost!", "What a nerve!", "Help!", "Ouch!", "Well I never!", "What a disaster!", "I'm tired of all this!", and "Let me out of here!" An **exclamatory question** is a sentence that is interrogative in form but is an exclamation in meaning, as in "Isn't the baby beautiful!" and "Isn't it lovely!"

extra-

A prefix meaning "beyond, outside" as in extra-marital, extra-terrestrial, extra-curricular.

F

fable

A story that is intended to convey a moral lesson. Fables frequently feature animals that speak and act like human beings. Most famous are those of Aesop, a Phrygian slave (620–560 BC), who wrote such fables as "The Hare and the Tortoise" and "The Fox and the Grapes."

false friends

A term for words that have the same or similar forms in different languages but have different meanings in each. For example, the French word *abusif* and the English word "abusive" are false friends. *Abusif* does not mean "abusive" but "incorrect, illegal, unauthorized, excessive." Similarly, the French word *actuel* and the English "actual" are false friends. *Actuel* does not mean "actual" but "present-day." Similarly, the French *éventuel* and Italian *eventuale* are false friends with the English "eventual." *Eventuel* and *eventuale* do not mean "eventual" but "possible," while *sensible* in French and *sensibile* in Italian do not mean "sensible, having good sense or judgment" but "sensitive, tender, touchy."

feminine

The term for the GENDER that indicates female persons or animals. It is the opposite of "masculine." The feminine gender demands the use of the appropriate pronoun, including "she," "her," "hers," and "herself," as in "The girl tried to save the dog but *she* was unable to do so," "The woman hurt *her* leg," "Rachel said that the book was *hers*," and "The waitress cut *herself*."

The feminine forms of words, formed by adding *-ess*, used to be common but many such forms are now thought to be sexist. Words such as "author," "sculptor," "poet" are now considered to be neutral terms that can be used to refer to a man or a woman. Some -ess words are either still being used or are in a state of flux, as in "actress." See -ESS.

few and a few

These are not interchangeable. Both expressions mean "some, but not many," but they convey different impressions. **Few** is the opposite of "many," as in "We have few resources" and "We have few ideas left." **A few** conveys a more positive impression and is the opposite of "none," as in "A few people volunteered their services" and "We have not reached a definite decision but we have a few ideas in hand." The sentence "We have few ideas left" indicates a negative situation, that "we" are running out of "ideas," but the sentence "We have a few ideas in hand" conveys a positive impression.

fewer and less

These are liable to be used wrongly. **Fewer** means "a smaller number of" and should be used with plural nouns, as in "fewer problems," "fewer resources," "fewer fears," "fewer boxes," "fewer books," "fewer bottles," "fewer chairs." **Less** means "a smaller amount of" and should be used with singular nouns, as in "less responsibility," "less anxiety," "less work," "less milk," "less wood," "less material." It is a very common error to use less where fewer is correct, as in "less bottles" and "less people."

figurative

A term that refers to words that are not used literally. For example, "mine" in the sense of "excavation in the earth from which coal, tin, etc., is taken" is a literal use of the word. "Mine" in the sense of "He is a mine of information" is a figurative use of the word. There are many figurative expressions in English. These include "take the bull by the horns," "put one's shoulder to the wheel," "hide one's light under a bushel," "be in seventh heaven," "count one's chickens," "change horses in mid-stream," "blow hot and cold," "run with the hare and hunt with the hounds," "make the feathers fly," "put the cat among the pigeons," "cut corners," "cry over spilt milk," "jump on the bandwagon," "let the grass grow under one's feet," "drop a brick," "burn the midnight oil," "show a clean pair of heels," "turn one's coat," "drive a coach and horses through."

figure of speech

A form of expression used to heighten the effect of a statement. The most commonly known are SIMILES and METAPHORS, but there are many more, such as PERSONIFICATION. *See* individual entries for further information.

finite clause

A clause that contains a FINITE VERB, as in "when she sees him," "after she had defeated him," "as they were sitting there."

finite verb

A verb that has a tense and has a subject with which it agrees in number and person. For example "cries" is finite in the sentence "The child cries most of the time," and "looks" is finite in the sentence "The old man looks ill." However "go" in the sentence "He wants to go" is non-finite since it has no variation of tense and does not have a subject. Similarly, in the sentence "Sitting on the river-bank, he was lost in thought," "sitting" is non-finite.

first person

This refers to the person who is speaking or writing when referring to himself or herself. The **first person pronouns** are "I," "me," "myself," and "mine," with the plural forms being "we," "us," "ourselves," and "ours," as in
"*I* am going shopping," he said.
    and
"*We* have very little money left," she said to her husband.
    The **first person determiners** are "my" and "our," as in
"I forgot to bring *my* notebook"
    and
"We must remember to bring *our* books home."

fixed phrase *also called* set phrase

A phrase that has no, or virtually no, variants, as in "from bad to worse," "to and fro," "hither and thither," "horse and cart," "this and that," "alas and alack," "rough and ready."

-fold

A suffix meaning "times, multiplied by," as in fourfold, a hundred-fold.

for-

A prefix derived from Old English with several meanings. These include "prohibition," as in forbid; "abstention" as in forbear, forgo, forswear; "neglect," as in forsake; "excess, intensity," as in forlorn; and "away, off, apart," as in forgive.

fore-

A prefix derived from Old English meaning "before," as in forecast, forestall, foretell, forewarn, foregoing, forefathers. It can also mean "front," as in foreleg, forehead, forepart.

foreign expression

An expression that has been adopted into English but not "naturalized" and is sometimes written in italic type, as in *bête noire* (a fear or obsession), *rara avis* (a rarity), *en passant* (in passing), *hors de combat* (out of the contest, disabled), *en route* (on the way), *bon mot* (witty saying), *in toto* (completely), *in flagrante delicto* (in the very act of committing an offense), *enfant terrible* (a person who causes embarrassment by indiscreet or outrageous behavior), *en famille* (with one's family), *inter alia* (among other things).

foreign plural

A plural of a word in English that has retained the plural form of the foreign word from which the English word has been derived. Examples include "phenomena" from "phenomenon," "crises" from "crisis," and "criteria" from "criterion." There is a modern tendency to anglicize some of the foreign plural forms. In some cases the foreign plural form and the anglicized form exist alongside each other as "formulae/formulas," "thesauri/thesauruses," "radii/radiuses," "indices/indexes," and "bureaux/bureaus."

-form

A suffix meaning "having the form of," as in cruciform, or "having such a number of," as in uniform, multiform.

formal

The term used to refer to speech and writing that is characterized by more complicated and more difficult language and by more complicated grammatical structures. Short forms and contractions are avoided in formal speech and writing. *See* INFORMAL.

formula

A set phrase that is used in certain conventions, as in "How do you do?", "Yours faithfully," "Yours sincerely," "Kind regards," "See you later," "Nice to see you!", and "Many happy returns."

form word *see* **function word**.

fragmentary sentence *see* **major sentence**.

-free

A suffix used to form adjectives indicating "absence of, freedom from," as in carefree, trouble-free, anxiety-free, tax-free, duty-free, additive-free, lead-free.

frequentative

A term referring to a verb that expresses frequent repetition of an action. In English the verb endings *-le* and *-el* sometimes indicate the frequentative form, as in "waddle" from "wade," "sparkle" from "spark," "crackle" from "crack," and "dazzle" from "daze." The ending *-er* can also indicate the frequentative form, as in "stutter," "spatter," and "batter."

-friendly

A modern suffix formed on analogy with "user-friendly" to mean "helpful to, supporting," as in child-friendly, environment-friendly, ozone-friendly.

-ful

A suffix indicating "the amount that fills something," as in bucketful, basinful, handful, spoonful, bagful, pocketful. It can also mean "full of," as in beautiful, truthful, scornful. It can also mean "having the qualities of," as in masterful, and "apt to, able to," as in forgetful, mournful, useful.

full stop *see* **period**.

function word

A word that has very little meaning but is primarily of grammatical significance and merely performs a "function" in a sentence. Function words include determiners, and prepositions such as in, on, and up. Words that are not function words are sometimes known as **content words**.

A function word is also known as a **form word** or a **structure word**.

future perfect tense

The TENSE of a verb that is formed by "will" or "shall" together with the perfect tense, as in "They will have been married ten years next week," "You will have finished work by this time tomorrow," "By the time Juanita arrives here she will have been traveling non-stop for 48 hours."

future tense

The TENSE of a verb that describes actions or states that will occur at some future time. It is marked by "will" and "shall." Traditionally "shall" was used with subjects in the first person, as in "I shall see you tomorrow" and "We shall go there next week," and "will" was used with subjects in the second and third person, as in "You will find out next week," "He will recognize her when he sees her," and "They will be on the next train." Formerly "will" was used with the first person and "shall" with the second and third person to indicate emphasis or insistence, as in "I *will* go on my own" and "We *will* be able to afford it"; "You *shall* pay what you owe" and "The children *shall* get a vacation." In modern usage "shall" is usually used only for emphasis or insistence, whether with the first, second, or third person, except in formal contexts. Otherwise "will" is used, as in "I will go tomorrow," "We will have to see," "You will be surprised," and "They will be on their way by now."

The future tense can also be marked by "be about to" plus the infinitive of the relevant verb or "be going to" plus the infinitive of the relevant verb. Examples include "We are about to leave for work," "They are about to go on vacation," "She is going to be late," and "They are going to demolish the building."

G

-gate

A modern suffix that is added to a noun to indicate something scandalous. Most of the words so formed are short-lived and forgotten about almost as soon as they are invented. In modern usage they are frequently used to apply to sexual scandals, but originally -gate was restricted to some form of political scandal. The suffix is derived from Watergate, and refers to a political scandal during President Richard Nixon's re-election campaign in 1972, when Republican agents were caught breaking into the headquarters of the Democratic Party in Washington, which were in a building called the Watergate Building. The uncovering of the attempts to cover up the break-in led to President Nixon's resignation.

gemination

The doubling of consonants before a suffix. *See* DOUBLING OF CONSONANTS.

gender

In the English language this usually refers to the natural distinctions of sex (or absence of sex) that exist, and nouns are classified according to these distinctions—masculine, feminine, and neuter. Thus, "man," "boy," "king," "prince," "emperor," "duke," "heir," "son," "brother," "father," "nephew," "husband," "bridegroom," "widower," "hero," "cock," "drake," "fox," and "lion" are masculine nouns. Similarly, "girl," "woman," "queen," "princess," "empress," "duchess," "heiress," "daughter," "sister," "mother," "niece," "wife," "bride," "widow," "heroine," "hen," "duck," "vixen," and "lioness" are feminine nouns. Similarly, "table," "chair," "desk," "carpet," "window," "lamp," "car," "store," "dress," "tie," "newspaper," "book," "building," and "town" are all neuter.

Some nouns in English can refer either to a man or a woman, unless the sex is indicated in the context. Such neutral nouns are sometimes said to have DUAL GENDER. Examples include "author," "singer," "poet," "sculptor," "proprietor," "teacher," "parent," "cousin," "adult," and "child." Some nouns in this category were formerly automatically assumed to be masculine and several of them had feminine forms, such as "authoress," "poetess," "sculptress," and "proprietrix." In modern times this was felt to be sexist and many of these feminine forms are now rarely used, for example, "authoress" and "poetess." However some, such as actress and waitress, are still in common use. *See* -ESS.

In many languages grammatical gender plays a major part. In French, for example, all nouns are divided into masculine and feminine, and there is no neuter classification. Masculine nouns are preceded by *le* (definite article). Thus "ceiling" is masculine (*le plafond*), "hat" is masculine (*le chapeau*), and "book" is masculine (*le livre*). Feminine nouns are preceded by *la* (definite article). Thus "door" is feminine (*la porte*), "dress" is feminine (*la robe*), and "window" is feminine (*la fenêtre*).

In German there are three grammatical genders—masculine, feminine, and neuter. Masculine nouns are preceded by *der* (definite article) as *der Stuhl* (the chair); feminine nouns are preceded by *die* (definite article) as *die Brücke* (the bridge); neuter nouns are preceded by *das*, as *das Brot* (bread).

Grammatical gender in English is not relevant except in the third personal singular pronouns, as "he/him/his/himself," "she/her/hers/herself," and "it/it/its/itself." Traditionally "he," etc., was considered an acceptable pronoun not just for nouns of the masculine gender, but also for those of neutral or dual gender as well. Thus "Every student must check that he has registered for the test" was considered acceptable, as was "Each passenger must be responsible for his own baggage." Nowadays such sentences are considered sexist. In order to avoid this, some people use the "he/she," "his/her," etc., convention, as in "Every employee must supply his/her own transport" and "Each candidate must hand in his/her application form now." People who feel this is clumsy sometimes prefer to be ungrammatical and use a plural pronoun, as in

"Every writer was told to collect their manuscripts in person" and "Every student was told that they would have to be back in school by four o'clock." It is sometimes possible to avoid being both sexist and ungrammatical by rephrasing such sentences in the plural, as in "All students were told that they would have to be back in school by four o'clock."

genitive case

A case that indicates possession or ownership. It is usually marked by s and an apostrophe. Many spelling errors center on the position of the s in relation to the apostrophe.

Nouns in the genitive case are usually formed by adding 's to the singular noun, as in "the girl's mother," and "Peter's car"; by adding an apostrophe to plural nouns that end in s, as in "all the teachers' cars" and "the doctors' surgeries"; by adding 's to irregular plural nouns that do not end in s, as in "women's shoes."

In the genitive form of a name or singular noun that ends in s, x, or z, the apostrophe may or may not be followed by s. In words of one syllable the final s is usually added, as in "James's house," "the fox's lair," "Roz's dress."

The final s is most frequently omitted in names, particularly in names of three or more syllables, as in "Euripides' plays."

In many cases the presence or absence of final s is a matter of convention.

Apostrophes are often omitted wrongly in modern usage, particularly in the media and by advertisers, as in "womens hairdressers," "childrens helpings." In addition, apostrophes are frequently added erroneously (as in "potatoe's for sale" and "Beware of the dog's"). This is partly because people are unsure about when and when not to use them and partly because of a modern tendency to punctuate as little as possible.

A group genitive occurs when more than one noun is involved, as in "Gilbert and Sullivan's comic operas." Note there is only one apostrophe s.

The alternate genitive construction involves the use of "of," as in "the mother of the girl," "the uncle of the little girl," "the pages of the newspaper," and "the leg of the chair." In general, proper nouns and animate beings tend to take the apostrophe and s ending and inanimate objects tend to take the "of" construction.

geo-

A prefix derived from Greek indicating "earth," as in geography, geology, geomagnetic, geophysics.

geographical features

These should be written with initial capital letters. They include the common nouns that are part of the name of the feature, as in Niagara Falls, Atlantic Ocean, Grand Canyon, Mount Everest, and Devil's Island.

gerund

The -ing form of a verb when it functions as a noun. It is sometimes known as a **verbal noun**. It has the same form as the present participle but has a different function. For example, in the sentence "He was jogging down the road," "jogging" is the present participle in the verb phrase "was jogging," but in the sentence "Running is his idea of relaxation," "running" is a gerund because it acts as a noun as the subject of the sentence. Similarly, in the sentence "We were smoking when the teacher found us," "smoking" is the present participle in the verb phrase "were smoking," but in the sentence "We were told that smoking is bad for our health," "smoking" is a gerund since it acts as a noun as the subject of the clause.

get

This verb is sometimes used to form the passive voice instead of the verb "to be." The use of the verb "to get" to form the passive, as in "They get married tomorrow," "Our team got beaten today," and "We got swindled by the con man" is sometimes considered to be more informal than the use of "be." Often there is more action involved when the get construction is used than when be is used, since get is a more dynamic verb, as in "She was late leaving the pub because she got involved in an argument" and in "It was her own fault that she got arrested by the police. She hit one of the officers."

Get is frequently over-used. Such over-use should be avoided, particularly in formal contexts. Get can often be replaced by a synonym such as "obtain," "acquire," "receive," "get hold of," etc. Thus, "If you are getting into money difficulties you should get some financial advice. Perhaps you could get a bank loan" could be rephrased as "If you are in financial difficulty you should obtain some financial help. Perhaps you could receive a bank loan."

Got, the past tense of get, is often used unnecessarily, as in "She has got red hair and freckles" and "We have got enough food to last us the week." In these sentences "has" and "have" are sufficient on their own.

gliding vowel *means the same as* diphthong.

goal

This can be used to describe the recipient of the action of a verb, the opposite of "agent" or "actor." Thus, in the sentence "The boy hit the girl," "boy" is the agent or actor and "girl" is the goal. Similarly, in the sentence "The dog bit the postman," "dog" is the agent or actor and "postman" is the goal.

gobbledygook

A noun that is used informally to refer to pretentious and convoluted language of the type that is found in official documents and reports. It is extremely difficult to understand and should be avoided and "plain English" used instead.

govern

A term that is used of a verb or preposition in relation to a noun or pronoun to indicate that the verb or preposition has a noun or pronoun depending on it. Thus, in the phrase "on the table," "on" is said to govern "table."

gradable

A term that is used of adjectives and adverbs to mean that they can take degrees of comparison. Thus "clean" is a gradable adjective since it has a comparative form (cleaner) and a superlative form (cleanest). "Soon" is a gradable adverb since it has a comparative form (sooner) and a superlative form (soonest). Such words as "supreme," which cannot normally have a comparative or superlative form, are called **non-gradable**.

-gram

A suffix derived from Greek indicating "writing" or "drawing," as in telegram, electrocardiogram, diagram.

-graph

A suffix derived from Greek indicating "written, recorded, represented," as in autograph, monograph, photograph. It is also used to indicate "an instrument that records," as in seismograph, tachograph, cardiograph.

group noun *means the same as* **collective noun**.

gynec-, gyneco-

A prefix derived from Greek indicating "female, woman," as in gynecology, gynecium.

H

habitual

A term used to refer to the action of a verb that occurs regularly and repeatedly. The **habitual present** is found in such sentences as "He goes to bed at ten every night," "She always walks to work" and "The old man sleeps all day." This is in contrast to the **stative present**, which indicates the action of the verb that occurs at all times, as in "Cows chew the cud," "Water becomes ice when it freezes," "Children grow up," and "We all die." Examples of the **habitual past** tense include; "They traveled by train to work all their lives," "We worked twelve hours a day on that project" and "She studied night and day for the tests."

haiku

A short Japanese poem in three unrhymed lines with an exact number of syllables per line, the syllable pattern being 5-7-5. The traditional subject matter is usually something to do with nature. A master of the form was the 17th-century Japanese poet Basho, and the following is one of his haiku:

> The|white|chry|san|themum
> Even|when|lif|ted|to|the|eye
> Re|mains|im|macu|late.

half *and* halve

These are liable to be confused. **Half** is a noun and **halve** is a verb. Half is followed by a singular noun when it is referring to an amount, as in "Half of the milk has gone sour" and "Half the money is hers." It is followed by a plural verb when it is referring to a number, as in "Half of the people are still undecided" and "Half of the candies are for the younger children." The plural of half is **halves**, as in "They cut the oranges in two and distributed the halves to the members of the two teams."

The plural noun halves is liable to be confused with the verb **halve**. Examples of the noun halves include "They served halves of grapefruit for breakfast" and "He split the estate into halves and left it to his son and daughter." Examples of the verb halve include "Halve the grapefruit for breakfast" and "He decided to halve his estate between his son and daughter."

-hand

A suffix meaning "worker," as in deck hand, farmhand, and cowhand. It can also mean "position," as in right-hand and left-hand.

hanged *and* hung

These are both past tense and past participles of the verb "to hang" but they are not interchangeable. **Hung** is the more usual form, as in "The children hung their outdoor clothes on pegs outside the classroom," "They hung the portrait of her father in the dining room," "Dark clouds of smoke hung over the city," and "The boy has hung out with the same crowd of friends for years."

Hanged is restricted to the meaning "suspended by the neck until dead," as in "They hanged him for the murder of his wife in the 1920s," "The murderer took his own life before he could be hanged," "They had to break the news to the children that their father had hanged himself," and "She hanged herself while the balance of her mind was disturbed."

hanging participle *see* dangling participle.

have

A verb that has several functions. A major use is its part in forming the "perfect tense" and "past perfect tense," or "pluperfect tense," of other verb tenses. It does this in conjunction with the "past participle" of the verb in question.

The perfect tense of a verb is formed by the present tense of the verb have and the past participle of the verb. Examples include "We have acted wisely," "They have beaten the opposition," "The police have caught the thieves," "The old man has died," "The child has eaten all the food," "The baby has fallen downstairs,"

"They have grabbed all the bargains," "You have hated him for years," and "He has indicated that he is going to retire." The past perfect or pluperfect is formed by the past tense of the verb have and the past participle of the verb in question, as in "He had jumped over the fence," "They had kicked in the door," "The boy had led the other children to safety," "His mother had made the cake," "The principal had punished the students," and "They had rushed into buying a new house." Both perfect tenses and past perfect or pluperfect tenses are often contracted in speech or in informal written English, as in "We've had enough for today," "You've damaged the suitcase," "You've missed the bus," "He's lost his pocketbook," "She's arrived too late," "They'd left before the news came through," "She'd married without telling her parents," "He'd packed the goods himself," and "You'd locked the door without realizing it."

Have is often used in the phrase **have to** in the sense that something must be done. In the present tense have to can be used instead of "must," as in "You have to leave now," "We have to clear this mess up," "He has to catch the next train," and "The goods have to be sold today." If the "something that must be done" refers to the future, the verb **will have to** is used, as in "He will have to leave now to get there on time," "The old man will have to go to the hospital," and "They'll have to move out of the house when her parents return." If the "something that must be done" refers to the past, **had to** is used, as in "We had to take the injured man to the hospital," "They had to endure freezing conditions on the mountain," "They'd to take a reduction in salary," and "We'd to wait all day for the maintenance man to appear."

Have is also used in the sense of "possess" or "own," as in "He has a swimming pool behind his house," "She has a huge wardrobe," "We have enough food," and "They have four cars." In spoken or in informal English "have got" is often used, as in "They've got the largest house in the street," "We've got problems now," "They haven't got time." This use should be avoided in formal English.

Have is also used to indicate suffering from an illness or disease, as in "The child has measles," "Her father has flu," and "She has heart disease." Have can also indicate that an activity is taking place, as in "She's having a shower," "We're having a party," "She is having a baby," and "They are having a dinner party."

due to leave" and "All students were advised that they should apply for a college place by March."

he

A personal pronoun that is used as the subject of a sentence or clause to refer to a man, boy, etc. It is thus said to be a "masculine" personal pronoun. Since he refers to a third party and does not refer to the speaker or the person being addressed, it is a third-person pronoun. Examples include "Darren is quite nice but he can be boring," "Bob has a new job and he is very pleased" and "He is rich now but his parents are still very poor."

He traditionally was used not only to refer to nouns relating to the masculine sex but also to nouns that are now regarded as being neutral or of DUAL GENDER. Such nouns include "architect," "artist," "athlete," "doctor," "passenger," "parent," "student," "singer." Without further information from the context it is impossible to know to which sex such nouns are referring. In modern usage it is regarded as sexist to assume such words to be masculine by using he to refer to one of them unless the context indicates that the noun in question refers to a man or boy. Formerly it was considered acceptable to write or say "Send a message to the architect who designed the building that he is to attend the meeting" whether or not the writer or speaker knew that the architect was a man. Similarly, it was considered acceptable to write or say "Please tell the doctor that he is to come straight away" whether or not the speaker or writer knew that the doctor was in fact a man. Nowadays this convention is considered sexist. In order to avoid sexism, it is possible to use the convention "he/she," as in "Every student was told that he/she was to be smartly dressed for the occasion," "Each passenger was informed that he/she was to arrive ten minutes before the bus was due to leave" and "Tell the doctor that he/she is required urgently." However this convention is regarded by some people as being clumsy, particularly in spoken English or in informal written English. Some people prefer to be ungrammatical and use the plural personal pronoun "they" instead of "he/she" in certain situations, as in "Every passenger was told that they had to arrive ten minutes before the bus was due to leave" and "Every student was advised that they should apply for a college place by March." In some cases it may be possible to rephrase sentences and avoid being either sexist or ungrammatical, as in "All the passengers were told that they should arrive ten minutes before the bus was due to leave" and "All students were advised that they should apply for a college place by March."

heading

A word, phrase, or sentence put at the top of a page, chapter, section, etc., of a book or other printed document. These are sometimes written with initial capital letters (except for articles or prepositions), as in "Annual Report," "Department Budget for the Year," "The Year Ahead," "What Went Wrong," "Company Plans," "Trading Outlook Overseas," but this is a matter of taste or of house style of the company or organization involved. Some people prefer to use lower-case letters except for the first word, as in "Sales targets for the year," "A review of export markets," and "The way forward." Headings can be underlined or placed in italic type or bold type to highlight them on the page.

headline

The name given to the title of a newspaper article. From the very nature of headlines they are short, partly because of shortage of space and partly to capture the attention of the would-be reader. In order to achieve this, the definite and indefinite articles and other minor words tend to be omitted, the future tense represented by a to-infinitive, as in "Prescription charges to rise," and the present tenses used for past events. **Headline language**, particularly that of tabloid newspapers, which has to be especially succinct and eye-catching, can have an effect on the general language. Thus expressions such as "tug-of-love," which describes the state of a child whose custody is being bitterly fought over by both parents, is now quite common in the general language but started out as a headline term. Other expressions that are typical of the language of the headlines include "killing spree," which describes someone who loses control and kills, usually by shooting, several people indiscriminately, as in "Local gunman goes on killing spree." The language and style of headlines is frequently known as **headlinese**.

headword

A word that is at the head of an entry in a dictionary or other reference book. It is also known as "entry word" and is usually written in bold type so that it stands out on the page and is readily identifiable.

helping verb *another name for* auxiliary verb.

hem-, hemo-
A prefix derived from Greek meaning "blood," as in hemorrhage, hematology, hematoma.

hemi-
A prefix derived from Greek meaning "half," as in hemisphere, hemiplegia.

hendiadys
A figure of speech in which two nouns joined by "and" are used to express an idea that would normally be expressed by the use of an adjective and a noun, as in "through storm and weather" instead of "through stormy weather."

her
A personal pronoun. It is the third person singular, is feminine in gender, and acts as the object in a sentence, as in "We saw her yesterday," "I don't know her," "He hardly ever sees her," "Please give this book to her," "Our daughter sometimes plays with her," and "We do not want her to come to the meeting." *See* HE; SHE.

hers
A personal pronoun. It is the third person singular, feminine in gender, and is in the possessive case. "The car is not hers," "I forgot my book but I don't want to borrow hers," "This is my seat and that is hers," and "These clothes are hers." *See* HIS; HER and POSSESSIVE.

he/she *see* he.

hetero-
A prefix derived from Greek meaning "other, another, different," as in heterodox, heterosexual.

hexa-
A prefix derived from Greek meaning "six," as in hexagram, hexagon.

hiatus

A break in pronunciation between two vowels that come together in different syllables, as in "Goyaesque" and "cooperate."

him

The third person masculine personal pronoun when used as the object of a sentence or clause, as in "She shot him," "When the police caught the thief they arrested him" and "His parents punished him after the boy stole the money." Traditionally him was used to apply not only to masculine nouns, such as "man" and "boy," but also to nouns that are said to be "of dual gender." These include "architect," "artist," "parent," "passenger," and "student." Without further information from the context, it is not possible for the speaker or writer to know the sex of the person referred to by one of these words. Formerly it was acceptable to write or say "The artist must bring an easel with him" and "Each student must bring food with him." In modern usage this convention is considered sexist and there is a modern convention that him/her" should be used instead to avoid sexism, as in "The artist must bring an easel with him/her" and "Each student must bring food with "him/her." This convention is felt by some people to be clumsy, particularly in spoken or in informal written English. Some people prefer to be ungrammatical and use the plural personal pronoun "them" instead, as in "The artist must bring an easel with them" and "Each student must bring food with them." In some situations it is possible to avoid being either sexist or ungrammatical by rephrasing the sentence, as in "All artists must bring easels with them" and "All students must bring food with them." *See* HE.

him/her *see* him.

his

The third personal masculine pronoun when used to indicate possession, as in "He has hurt his leg," "The boy has taken his books home," and "Where has your father left his tools?" Traditionally his was used to refer not only to masculine nouns, such as "man," "boy," etc., but to what are known as nouns "of dual gender." These include "architect," "artist," "parent," "passenger," and "student." Without further information from the context it is not possible for the speaker or the writer to know the sex of the person referred to by one of these words. Formerly it was considered acceptable to use his in such situations, as in "Every student has to supply his own sports equipment" and "Every passenger is responsible for his own baggage." In modern usage this is now considered sexist and there is a modern convention that "his/her" should be used instead to avoid sexism, as in "Every student has to supply his/her own sports equipment" and "Every passenger is responsible for his/her own baggage." This convention is felt by some people to be clumsy, particularly when used in spoken English or in informal written English. Some people prefer to be ungrammatical and use the plural personal pronoun "their," as in "Every student must supply their own sports equipment" and "Every passenger is to be responsible for their own baggage." In some situations it is possible to avoid being sexist, clumsy, and ungrammatical by rephrasing the sentence, as in "All students must supply their own sports equipment" and "All passengers are to be responsible for their own baggage."

his/her *see* his.

holidays
These, in the sense of public holidays or festivals, should be written with an initial capital letter, as in Christmas Day, Thanksgiving Day, New Year's Day, and Independence Day.

holo-
A prefix meaning "complete, whole," as in holistic.

homo-
A prefix derived from Greek meaning "same," as in homogenous, homonym, homograph, homology, homophone, homosexual.

homograph
A word that is spelt the same as another word but has a different meaning and pronunciation. Homographs include:

bow, pronounced to rhyme with "how," a verb meaning "to bend the head or body as a sign of respect or in greeting, etc.," as in "The visitors bowed to the emperor" and "The mourners bowed their heads as the coffin was lowered into the grave."

bow, pronounced to rhyme with "low," a noun meaning "a looped knot, a ribbon tied in this way," as in "She tied her hair in a bow" and "She wears blue bows in her hair."

lead, pronounced "leed," a verb meaning "to show the way," as in "The guide will lead you down the mountain."

lead, pronounced "led," a noun meaning "a type of grayish metal," as in "They are going to remove any water pipes made of lead."

row, pronounced to rhyme with "low," a noun meaning "a number of people or things arranged in a line," as in "The princess sat in the front row."

row, pronounced to rhyme with "how," a noun meaning "a quarrel, a disagreement," as in "He has had a row with his neighbor over repairs to the garden wall."

slough, pronounced to rhyme with "rough," a verb meaning "to cast off," as in "The snake had sloughed off its old skin."

slough, pronounced to rhyme with "how," a noun meaning "a swamp," as in "Get bogged down in a slough" and "in the Slough of Despond."

sow, pronounced to rhyme with "low," a verb meaning "to scatter seeds in the earth," as in "In the spring the gardener sowed some flower seeds in the front garden."

sow, pronounced to rhyme with "how," a noun meaning "a female pig," as in "The sow is in the pigsty with her piglets."

homonym

A word that has the same spelling and the same pronunciation as another word but has a different meaning from it. Examples include:

bill, a noun meaning "a written statement of money owed," as in "You must pay the bill for the conversion work immediately," or "a written or printed advertisement," as in "We were asked to deliver handbills advertising the play."

bill, a noun meaning "a bird's beak," as in "The seagull has injured its bill."

fair, an adjective meaning "attractive," as in "fair young women"; "light in color," as in "She has fair hair"; "fine, not raining," as in "I hope it keeps fair"; "just, free from prejudice," as in "We felt that the umpire came to a fair decision."

fair, a noun meaning "a market held regularly in the same place, often with stalls, entertainments, and rides" (now often simply applying to an event with entertainments and rides without the market), as in "He won a coconut at the fair"; "a trade exhibition," as in "the New York World's Fair."

pulse, a noun meaning "the throbbing caused by the contractions of the heart," as in "The patient has a weak pulse."

pulse, a noun meaning "the edible seeds of any of various crops of the pea family, as lentils, peas, and beans," as in "Vegetarians eat a lot of food made with pulses."

row, a verb meaning "to propel a boat by means of oars," as in "He plans to row across the Atlantic single-handed."

row, a noun meaning "a number of people or things arranged in a line," as in "We tried to get into the front row to watch the procession" and "The gardener has planted rows of cabbages."

homophone

The term for a word that is pronounced in the same way as another but is spelt in a different way and has a different meaning. Some examples of homophones include the following:

aisle, a noun meaning "a passage between rows of seats in a church, theater, airplane, etc.," as in "The bride walked down the aisle on her father's arm."

isle, a noun meaning "an island," as in "Isle Royale."

ail, a verb meaning "to be ill," as in "The old woman is ailing"; "to trouble," as in "What ails you?"

ale, a noun meaning "a kind of beer," as in "a pint of foaming ale."

alter, a verb meaning "to change," as in "They had to alter their plans."

altar, a noun meaning "in the Christian church, the table on which the bread and wine are consecrated for Communion and which serves as the center of worship," as in "The priest moved to the altar, from where he dispensed Communion," "There is a holy painting above the altar"; or "a raised structure on which sacrifices are made or incense burned in worship," as in "The Druids made human sacrifices on the altar of their gods."

blew, a verb, the past tense of the verb "blow," as in "They blew the trumpets loudly."

blue, a noun and adjective meaning "a color of the shade of a clear sky," as in "She wore a blue dress."

boar, a noun meaning "a male pig," as in "a dish made with wild boar."

bore, a verb meaning "to make tired and uninterested," as in "The audience was obviously bored by the rather academic lecture."

bore, a verb, the past tense of the verb "bear," as in "They bore their troubles lightly."

cereal, a noun meaning "a plant yielding grain suitable for food," as in "countries which grow cereal crops" and "a prepared food made with grain," as in "We usually have cereal for breakfast."

serial, a noun meaning "a story or television play which is published or appears in regular parts," as in "the final installment of the magazine serial that I was following."

cite, a verb meaning "to quote or mention by way of example or proof," as in "The lawyer cited a previous case to try to get his client off."

sight, a noun meaning "the act of seeing," as in "They recognized him at first sight."

site, a noun meaning "a location, place," as in "They have found a site for the new factory."

feat, a noun meaning "a notable act or deed," as in "The old man received an award for his courageous feat."

feet, a noun, the plural form of "foot," as in "The child got her feet wet from wading in the puddle."

none, a pronoun meaning "not any," as in "They are demanding money but we have none."

nun, a noun meaning "a woman who joins a religious order and takes vows of poverty, chastity, and obedience," as in "She gave up the world to become a nun."

know, a verb meaning "to have understanding or knowledge of," as in "He is the only one who knows the true facts of the situation," and "to be acquainted with," as in "I met her once but I don't really know her."

no, an adjective meaning "not any," as in "We have no food left."

rite, a noun meaning "a ceremonial act or words," as in "rites involving witchcraft."

right, an adjective meaning "correct," as in "Very few people gave the right answer to the question."

write, a verb meaning "to form readable characters," as in "He writes regularly for the newspapers."

stare, a verb and noun meaning "to look fixedly" and "a fixed gaze," as in "She stared at him in disbelief when he told her the news" and "She was unsettled by his intent stare."

stair, a noun meaning "a flight of steps," as in "The old lady is too feeble to climb the stair to her bedroom."

-hood

A suffix meaning "state, condition," as in babyhood, childhood, manhood, priesthood, widowhood, womanhood.

hybrid

A word that is formed from words or elements derived from different languages, such as "television."

hydro-

A prefix derived from Greek meaning "water, as in hydro-electric and hydrophobia. It also means "hydrogen," as in hydrochloride.

hyper-

A prefix derived from Greek meaning "over, above," as in hyperbole, hyperactive, hypercritical, hyperinflation, hypersensitive.

hyperbole

A figure of speech consisting of exaggeration or over-statement, used for emphasis, as in "I could eat a horse" and in "I am boiling in this heat."

hyphen

A small stroke (-) that is used to join two words together or to indicate that a word has been broken at the end of a line because of lack of space. It is used in a variety of situations.

The hyphen is used as the prefixed element in a proper noun, as in "pre-Christian," "post-Renaissance," "anti-British," "anti-Semitic," "pro-French," and "pro-Marxism." It is also used before dates or numbers, as in "pre-1914," "pre-1066," "post-1920," "post-1945." It is also used before abbreviations, as in "pro-KGB," "anti-U.S."

The hyphen is used for clarification. Some words are ambiguous without the presence of a hyphen. For example, "re-cover," as in "re-cover a chair," is spelt with a hyphen to differentiate it from "recover," as in "The accident victim is likely to recover." Similarly, it is used in "re-form," meaning "to form again," as in "They have decided to re-form the society which closed last year," to differentiate the word from "reform," meaning "to improve, to become better behaved," as in "He was wild as a young man but he has reformed now." Similarly "re-count" in the sense of "count again," as in "re-count the number of votes cast," is spelt with a hyphen to differentiate it from "recount" in the sense of "tell," as in "recount what happened on the night of the accident."

The hyphen was formerly used to separate a prefix from the main element of a word if the main element begins with a vowel, as in "pre-eminent," but there is a growing tendency in modern usage to omit the hyphen in such cases. At the moment both "pre-eminent" and "preeminent" are found. However, if the omission of the hyphen results in double *i*, the hyphen is usually retained, as in "anti-inflationary" and "semi-insulated."

The hyphen was formerly used in words formed with the prefix *non-*, as in "non-functional," "non-political," "non-flammable," and "non-pollutant." However there is a growing tendency to omit the hyphen in such cases, as in "nonfunctional" and "nonpollutant." At the moment both forms of such words are common.

The hyphen is usually used with "ex-" in the sense of "former," as in "ex-wife" and "ex-president."

The hyphen is usually used when "self-" is prefixed to words, as in "self-styled," "a self-starter," and "self-evident."

Use or non-use of the hyphen is often a matter of choice, house style, or frequency of usage, as in "drawing-room" or "drawing room," and "dining-room" or "dining room." There is a modern tendency to punctuate less frequently than was formerly the case and so in modern usage use of the hyphen in such expressions is less frequent. The length of compounds often affects the inclusion or omission of the hyphen. Compounds of two short elements that are well-established words tend not to be hyphenated, as in "bedroom" and "toothbrush." Compound words with longer elements are more likely to be hyphenated, as in "engine-driver" and "carpet-layer."

Some fixed compounds of two or three or more words are always hyphenated, as in "son-in-law," "good-for-nothing," and "devil-may-care."

Some compounds formed from phrasal verbs are sometimes hyphenated and sometimes not. Thus both "take-over" and "take-over" are common, and "run-down" and "rundown" are both common. Again the use of the hyphen is a matter of choice. However some words formed from phrasal verbs are usually spelt without a hyphen, as in "breakthrough."

Compound adjectives consisting of two elements, the second of which ends in -ed, are usually hyphenated, as in "heavy-hearted," "fair-haired," "fair-minded," and "long-legged."

Compound adjectives when they are used before nouns are usually hyphenated, as in "oil-based paints," "solar-heated buildings" and "a chocolate-flavored milk shake."

Compounds containing some adverbs are usually hyphenated, sometimes to avoid ambiguity, as in "his best-known movie," a "well-known singer," "an ill-considered venture," and "a half-planned scheme."

Generally adjectives and participles preceded by an adverb are not hyphenated if the adverb ends in -ly, as in "a highly talented singer," "freshly squeezed orange juice," and "beautifully dressed young women."

In the case of two or more compound hyphenated adjectives with the same second element qualifying the same noun, the common element need not be repeated but the hyphen should be, as in "two- and three-bedroom apartments" and "long- and short-haired dogs."

The hyphen is used in compound numerals from 21 to 99 when they are written in full, as in "thirty-five dollars," "forty-four years," "sixty-seven miles," and "two hundred and forty-five applicants." Compound numbers such as "three hundred" and "two thousand" are not hyphenated.

Hyphens are used in fractions, as in "three-quarters," "two-thirds," and "seven-eighths."

Hyphens are also used in such number phrases as "a seventeenth-century play," "an eighteenth-century church," "a five-year contract," and a "tenth-grade student."

The other use of hyphens is to break words at the ends of lines. Formerly people were more careful about where they broke

words. Previously, words were broken up according to etymo-
logical principles, but there is a growing tendency to break words
according to how they are pronounced. Some dictionaries or
spelling dictionaries give help with the division and hyphenation
of individual words. General points are that one-syllable words
should not be divided and words should not be broken after the
first letter of a word or before the last letter. Care should be taken
not to break up words, for example by forming elements that are
words in their own right, in such a way as to mislead the reader.
Thus divisions such as "the-rapist" and "mans-laughter" should be
avoided.

hypo-

A prefix derived from Greek meaning "under," as in hypothermia,
hypodermic.

I

I *and* me

These are liable to be confused. They are both parts of the first person singular pronoun, but I acts as the subject of a sentence and me as the object. People often assume wrongly that me is less "polite" than I. This is probably because they have been taught that in answer to such questions as "Who is there?" the grammatically correct reply is "It is I." In fact, except in formal contexts, "It is me" is frequently found in modern usage, especially in spoken contexts. Confusion arises as to whether to use I or me after "between." Since "between" is followed by an object, me is the correct form. Thus it is correct to say, "Just between you and me, I think he is dishonest." On the other hand, me, being an object, should not be used in such sentences as "You and I have both been invited," "May Julie and I play?" and "The children and I are going to join you." Me should, however, be used in such sentences as "The cake was made by Ben and me," "They were sitting in front of my sister and me at the theater," and "My brother and father played against my mother and me," since in all these cases it is the object form of the first person singular that is required.

-ian

A suffix either indicating "a profession, occupation, or pastime," as in comedian, musician, optician, physician, or indicating "proper names," as in Dickensian, Orwellian, and Shakespearian.

-iana

A suffix form of -ANA, indicating "memorabilia or collections relating to people or places of note," as in Victoriana and Canadiana.

-ible *see* adjectives.

-ics

A suffix indicating "science" or "study," as in "acoustics," "electronics," "genetics," "obstetrics," "politics," and "physics."

ideogram

A written character that symbolizes a word or phrase without indicating the pronunciation, such as $, &, +.

idiolect

The speech habits, knowledge, and command of language of an individual. This can vary considerably from person to person. For example, one person might have a much more formal idiolect than another.

idiom

An expression whose meaning cannot be easily deduced from the individual meanings of the words it contains. Thus, in the expression "know the ropes" one can know what "know" means and know what "ropes" means without being able to deduce the meaning of "know the ropes." In fact, "know the ropes" is a nautical idiom. If a sailor was being taught the basics of seamanship in the days of sailing ships, he would have to be taught the mechanics of ropes, which were an important part of sailing in those days. Hence, "know the ropes" has come to mean "to understand the procedures and details involved in something," as in "When he first started the job, the trainee mechanic felt really awkward and useless, but when he knew the ropes he felt more confident and happier."

Similarly, one can easily understand the meanings of the various individual words in the expression "out on a limb," but it is not at all obvious that it means idiomatically "in a risky and often lonely position," this being a reference to someone being stuck in an isolated and precarious position on the branch of a tree. This idiom is found in sentences such as "The young designer has gone out on a limb and produced clothing that his superior says is too experimental for the mass market." Literally, it refers to a person or animal that has crawled so far out on a branch of a tree that he/she is in danger of falling or of not being able to crawl back to the main tree.

Similarly, in the expression "throw someone to the lions," one can easily understand the meanings of the various individual words without realizing that the expression means "deliberately to put someone in a difficult or dangerous position," as in "All the teachers were responsible for the change in policy with regard to school uniform but they threw the deputy head to the lions when they asked him to address a parents' meeting on the subject." In order to appreciate the meaning of the idiom fully, the reader or listener has to understand that the idiom refers to a supposed form of entertainment in ancient Rome, in which prisoners were thrown to hungry wild animals to be attacked and killed (while spectators looked on enthusiastically).

Similarly, in the expression "throw in the towel," one can easily understand the meanings of the various individual words without realizing that the phrase means "to give in, to admit defeat," as in "She tried to stand up to the bullies in her school but finally she threw in the towel and asked her parents to send her to another school." This idiom comes from the world of boxing in which "throwing in the towel" indicates a method of conceding defeat.

Similarly, understanding the individual words of the expression "sell someone down the river" will not help one to understand that it means "to betray or be disloyal to someone," as in "The bank robber who was caught by the police refused to sell his associates down the river." The origin here is slightly more obscure, in that it refers historically to slave owners in the Mississippi states who sold their slaves to buyers downstream in Louisiana, where living and working conditions were much harder.

Such idioms as "sell someone down the river" are known as "opaque idioms" since there is no resemblance between the meaning of the individual words of the idiom and the idiom itself. Idioms such as "keep a straight face" are known as "transparent idioms" since, although they are not to be interpreted literally, it is reasonably obvious what they mean.

i.e.

The abbreviation of the Latin phrase *id est*, which is used before explanations or amplifications of what has just been mentioned, as in "He was a mercenary in the war, i.e. he fought for money," and "She is agoraphobic, i.e. she is afraid of open spaces," and "He is a bibliophile, i.e. he loves books." It is usually spelt with a period after each of the letters.

if

A CONJUNCTION that is often used to introduce a subordinate ADVERBIAL CLAUSE of condition, as in "If he is talking of leaving, he must be unhappy," "If you tease the dog, it will bite you," "If he had realized that the weather was going to be so bad, he would not have gone on the expedition," "If I had been in charge, I would have fired him," and "If it were a better organized firm, things like that would not happen."

If can also introduce a "nominal" or "noun clause," as in "He asked if we objected" and "She inquired if we wanted to go."

-ify

A suffix indicating "making or becoming," as in beautify, clarify, dignify, purify, satisfy, and simplify.

imperative mood

The verb mood that expresses commands. The verbs in the following sentences are in the imperative mood: "Go away!," "Run faster!", "Answer me!", "Sit down!", "Please get out of here!" All these expressions with verbs in the imperative mood sound rather imperious or dictatorial and usually end with an exclamation point, but this is not true of all expressions with verbs in the imperative mood. For example, the following sentences all have verbs in the imperative mood: "Have another helping of ice cream," "Help yourself to more wine," "Just follow the yellow arrows to the Emergency Room," and "Turn right at the traffic circle." Sentences with verbs in the imperative mood are known as **imperative sentences**.

imperfect

A TENSE that denotes an action in progress but not complete. The term derives from the classification in Latin grammar and was traditionally applied to the "past imperfect," as in "They were standing there." The imperfect has now been largely superseded by the progressive/continuous tense, which is marked by the use of "be," plus the present participle. Continuous tenses are used when talking about temporary situations at a particular point in time, as in "They were waiting for the bus."

impersonal

A verb that is used with a formal subject, usually "it," as in "It is raining" and "They say it will snow tomorrow."

indefinite article

A and **an** are the forms of the indefinite article. The form a is used before words that begin with a consonant sound, as "a box," "a garden," "a road," "a wall." The form an is used before words that begin with a vowel sound, as "an apple," "an easel," "an ostrich," "an uncle." Note that it is the sound of the initial letter that matters and not the spelling. Thus a is used before words beginning with a *u* when they are pronounced with a *y* sound as though it were a consonant, as "a unit," "a usual occurrence." Similarly, an is used, for example, before words beginning with the letter *h* where this is not pronounced, as in "an heir," "an hour," "an honest man."

Formerly it was quite common to use an before words that begin with an *h* sound and also begin with an unstressed syllable, as in "an hotel (*ho-tel*)," "an historic (*his-tor-ik*) occasion," "an hereditary (*her-ed-it-ary*) disease." It is now more usual to use a in such cases and ignore the question of the unstressed syllable.

indefinite pronouns

These are used to refer to people or things without being specific as to exactly who or what they are. They include "everyone," "everybody," "everything," "anyone," "anybody," "anything," "somebody," "someone," "something," and "nobody," "no one," "nothing," as in "Everyone is to make a contribution," "Anyone can enter," "Something will turn up," and "Nobody cares."

independent clause

A clause that can stand alone and make sense without being dependent on another clause, as in "The children are safe." MAIN CLAUSES are independent clauses. Thus in the sentence "She is tired and she wants to go home," there are two independent clauses joined by "and." In the sentence "She will be able to rest when she gets home," "She will be able to rest" is an independent clause and "when she gets home" is a DEPENDENT CLAUSE. In the sentence "Because she is intelligent she thinks for herself," "she thinks for herself" is an independent clause and "because she is intelligent" is a dependent clause.

indicative mood

The MOOD of a verb that denotes making a statement. The following sentences have verbs in the indicative mood: "We are going on vacation tomorrow," "He was waiting for her husband," "They have lost the game" and "She will arrive this afternoon." The indicative mood is sometimes known as the **declarative mood**. The other moods are the IMPERATIVE mood and SUBJUNCTIVE MOOD.

indirect object

An object that can be preceded by "to" or "for." The indirect object usually refers to the person who benefits from an action or receives something as the result of it.

In the sentence "Her father gave the boy food," "boy" is the indirect object and "food" is the DIRECT OBJECT. The sentence could be rephrased as "Her father gave food to the boy." In the sentence "He bought his mother flowers," "his mother" is the indirect object and "flowers" is the direct object. The sentence could have been rephrased as "He bought flowers for his mother." In the sentence "They offered him a reward," "him" is the indirect object and "reward" is the direct object. The sentence could be rephrased as "They offered a reward to him."

indirect question

A question that is reported in INDIRECT SPEECH, as in "We asked them where they were going," "They inquired why we had come," and "They looked at us curiously and asked where we had come from." Note that a question mark is not used.

indirect speech *or* reported speech

A way of reporting what someone has said without using the actual words used by the speaker. There is usually an introductory verb and a subordinate "that" clause, as in "He said that he was going away," and "They announced that they were leaving next day." In DIRECT SPEECH these sentences would become "He said, 'I am going away,'" and "They announced, 'We are leaving tomorrow.'" When the change is made from direct speech to indirect speech, the pronouns, adverbs of time and place, and tenses are changed to accord with the viewpoint of the person doing the reporting.

infinitive

The BASE form of a verb when used without any indication of person, number, or tense. There are two forms of the infinitive. One is the **to infinitive** form, as in "They wished to leave," "I plan to go tomorrow," "We aim to please," and "They want to travel," "To know all is to forgive all," "To err is human," "Pull the lever to open," "You should bring a book to read," "The child has nothing to do," "She is not very nice to know," and "It is hard to believe that it happened." The other form of the infinitive is called the **bare infinitive**. This form consists of the base form of the verb without "to," as in "We saw him fall," "She watched him go," "They noticed him enter," "She heard him sigh," "They let him go," "I had better leave," "We dare not go back," and "Need we return?" *See* SPLIT INFINITIVE.

inflect

When applied to a word, this means to change form in order to indicate differences of tense, number, gender, case, etc. Nouns inflect for plural, as in "ships," "chairs," "houses," and "oxen"; nouns inflect for possessive, as in "boy's," "woman's," "teachers'," and "parents'"; some adjectives inflect for the comparative form, as in "brighter," "clearer," "shorter," and "taller"; verbs inflect for the third person singular present tense, as in "hears," "joins," "touches," and "kicks"; verbs inflect for the present participle, as in "hearing," "joining," "touching," and "kicking"; verbs inflect for the past participle, as in "heard," "joined," "touched," and "kicked."

inflection

The act of inflecting—*see* INFLECT. It also refers to an inflected form of a word or a suffix or other element used to inflect a word.

informal

The term to describe a spoken or written style of language that has a simpler grammatical structure and simpler vocabulary, often involving vocabulary that is colloquial in nature or even slang.

infra-

A prefix derived from Latin meaning "below, beneath," as in infrared, infrastructure.

-ing form

This form of a verb can be either a PRESENT PARTICIPLE or a gerund. Present participles are used in the formation of the progressive or continuous TENSES, as in "We were looking at the pictures," "Children were playing in the snow," "They are waiting for the bus," "Parents were showing their anger," "He has been sitting there for hours." Present participles can also be used in non-finite clauses or phrases, as in "Walking along, she did not have a care in the world," "Lying there, he thought about his life," "Sighing, he left the room," and "Smiling broadly, he congratulated his friend."

A large number of adjectives end in -ing. Many of these have the same form as the present participle of a transitive verb and are similar in meaning. Examples include "an amazing spectacle," "a boring show," "an interesting idea," "a tiring day," "an exhausting climb," and "aching limbs." Some -ing adjectives are related to intransitive verbs, as "existing problems," "increasing responsibilities," "dwindling resources," "an aging work force," and "prevailing circumstances." Some -ing adjectives are related to the forms of verbs but have different meanings from the verbs, as in "a becoming dress," "an engaging personality," "a dashing young man," and "a retiring disposition." Some -ing adjectives are not related to verbs at all. These include "appetizing," "enterprising," "impending," and "balding." Some -ing adjectives are used informally for emphasis, as in "a blithering idiot," "a stinking cold," and "a flaming cheek."

Gerunds act as nouns and are sometimes known as **verbal nouns**. Examples include "Smoking is bad for one's health," "Cycling is forbidden in the park," and "Swimming is her favorite sport."

intensifier

The term for an adverb that affects the degree of intensity of another word. Intensifiers include "thoroughly" in "We were thoroughly shocked by the news," "scarcely" in "We scarcely recognized them," and "totally" in "She was totally amazed."

inter-

A prefix of Latin origin indicating "between," as in intercity, inter-continental, and interstate.

interjection

A kind of EXCLAMATION. Sometimes they are formed by actual words and sometimes they simply consist of sounds indicating emotional noises. Examples of interjections include "Oh! I'm totally shocked!", "Gee! I'm surprised to hear that!", "Phew! It's hot!", "Ouch! That was my foot!", "Tut-tut! He shouldn't have done that!", and "Alas! She is dead."

International Phonetic Alphabet

A system of written symbols designed to enable the speech sounds of any language to be consistently represented. Some of the symbols are the ordinary letters of the Roman alphabet but some have been specially invented. The alphabet was first published in 1889 and is commonly known as **IPA**.

interrogation point *see* **question mark**.

interrogative adjective *or* determiner

An adjective or determiner that asks for information in relation to the nouns that it qualifies, as in "What dress did you choose in the end?", "What kind of book are you looking for?", "Which house do you like best?", "Which student won the prize?", "Whose bike was stolen?", and "Whose dog is that?"

interrogative adverb

An adverb that asks a question, as in "When did they leave?", "When does the meeting start?", "Where do they live?", "Where was the stolen car found?", "Where did you last see her?", "Why was she crying?", "Why have they been asked to leave?", "How is the invalid?", "How do you know that she has gone?" and "Wherever did you find that?"

interrogative pronoun

A pronoun that asks a question, as in "Who asked you to do that?", "Who broke the vase?", "What did he say?", "What happened next?", "Whose are those books?", "Whose is that old car?", "To whom was that remark addressed?", and "To whom did you address the packet?"

interrogative sentence

A sentence that asks a question, as in "Who is that?", "Where is he?", "Why have they appeared?", "What did they take away?", "Which do you prefer?", and "Whose baby is that?" Sentences that take the form of an interrogative question do not always seek information. Sometimes they are exclamations, as in "Did you ever see anything so beautiful?", "Isn't she sweet?", and "Aren't they lovely?" Sentences that take the form of questions may really be commands or directives, as in "Could you turn down that radio?", "Would you make less noise?", and "Could you get her a chair?" Sentences that take the form of questions may function as statements, as in "Isn't there always a reason?" and "Haven't we all experienced disappointment?" Some interrogative sentences are what is known as RHETORICAL QUESTIONS, which are asked purely for effect and require no answer, as in "Do you think I'm a fool?", "What is the point of life?", and "What is the world coming to?"

intra-

A prefix derived from Latin meaning "within," as intramuscular, intra-uterine, intravenous.

intransitive verb

A verb that does not take a DIRECT OBJECT, as in "Snow fell yesterday," "The children played in the sand," "The path climbed steeply," "Time will tell," "The situation worsened," "Things improved," and "Prices increased." Many verbs can be either TRANSITIVE or intransitive, according to the context. Thus "play" is intransitive in the sentence "The children played in the sand" but transitive in the sentence "The boy plays the piano." Similarly "climb" is intransitive in the sentence "The path climbs steeply" but transitive in the sentence "The mountaineers climbed Everest." Similarly "tell" is intransitive in the sentence "Time will tell" but transitive in the sentence "He will tell his life story."

introductory it

The use of "it" as the subject of a sentence in the absence of a meaningful subject. It is used particularly in sentences about time and the weather, as in "It is midnight," "It is dawn," "It is five o'clock," "It is twelve noon," "It is raining," "It was snowing," "It was windy," and "It was blowing a gale."

invariable

A word whose form does not vary by inflection. Such words include "sheep" and "but."

inversion

The reversal of the usual word order. It particularly refers to subjects and verbs. Inversion is used in questions, in some negative sentences, and for literary effect. In questions, an AUXILIARY VERB is usually put in front of the subject and the rest of the verb group is put after the subject, as in "Are you going to see her?" and "Have they inspected the goods yet?" The verb "to do" is frequently used in inversion, as in "Did he commit the crime?" and "Do they still believe that?" Examples of the use of inversion in negative sentences include "Seldom have I witnessed such an act of selfishness," "Never had she experienced such pain," and "Rarely do we have time to admire the beauty of the countryside." This use in negative sentences is rather formal.

Inversion frequently involves adverbial phrases of place, as in "Beyond the town stretched field after field," "Above them soared the eagle" and "Along the driveway grew multitudes of daffodils."

Inversion is also found in conditional clauses that are not introduced by a conjunction, as in "Had you arrived earlier you would have been in time for dinner" and "Had we some more money we could do more for the refugees."

inverted commas

These are used to enclose material that is part of DIRECT SPEECH. They can also be used instead of italic type in the titles of books, newspapers, magazines, plays, movies, musical works, works of art, etc., as in "New York Times," "Tom Sawyer" by Mark Twain, "The Taming of the Shrew," "Gladiator," and "Madame Butterfly." Inverted commas can also be used to emphasize or draw attention to a particular word or phrase, as in "She wants to know how to spell 'picnicked.'" Inverted commas can either be single or double. If a word, phrase, or passage is already contained within quotes, one should use the opposite style of inverted commas to the set already in use, as in "She asked how to pronounce 'controversy'" or "She asked how to pronounce 'controversy.'"

IPA *see* **International Phonetic Alphabet**.

irony

The use of a word or words to convey something that is completely different from the literal meaning, as in "I don't suppose you'd be interested to hear that your house has been burgled," "So you've crashed the car. Thanks! That's a great help!" *See also* DRAMATIC IRONY.

irregular adjective

An adjective that does not conform to the usual rules of forming the comparative and superlative (*see* COMPARISON OF ADJECTIVES). Many adjectives either add -*er* for the comparative and -*est* for the superlative, as in "taller," "shorter" and "tallest," "shortest" from "tall" and "short." Some adjectives form their comparatives with "more" and their superlatives with "most," as in "more beautiful," "more practical" and "most beautiful," "most practical." Irregular adjectives do not form their comparatives and superlatives in either of these ways. Irregular adjectives include:

positive	*comparative*	*superlative*
good	better	best
bad	worse	worst
little	less	least
many	more	most

irregular plural

The plural form of a noun that does not form its plural in the regular way. Most nouns in English add -*s* to the singular form to form the plural form, as in "boy" to "boys." Some add -*es* to the singular form to form the plural, as in "church" to "churches." Nouns ending in a consonant followed by -*y* have -*ies* as a regular plural ending. Thus "fairy" becomes "fairies" and "berry" becomes "berries." The foregoing are all examples of regular plurals.

Irregular plurals include words that are different in form from the singular forms and do not simply add an ending. These include "men" from "man," "women" from "woman," and "mice" from "mouse." Some irregular plurals are formed by changing the vowel of the singular forms, as in "feet" from "foot," "geese" from "goose," and "teeth" from "tooth." Some irregular plural forms are formed by adding -en, as in "oxen" from "ox" and "children" from "child." Some nouns ending in -f form plurals in -ves, as in "loaf" to "loaves," "half" to "halves," "wife" to "wives," and "wolf" to "wolves," but some have alternate endings, as "hoof" to either "hoofs" or "hooves," and some form regular plurals unchanged, as "roof" to "roofs." Some irregular plural forms are the original foreign plural forms of words adopted into English, for example "stimuli" from "stimulus," "phenomena" from "phenomenon," "criteria" from "criterion," "larvae" from "larva." In modern usage there is a growing tendency to anglicize the plural forms of foreign words. Many of these co-exist with the plural form, for example "thesauruses" and "thesauri," "formulas" and "formulae," and "indexes" and "indices." Sometimes the anglicized plural formed according to the regular English rules differs slightly in meaning from the irregular foreign plural. Thus "indexes" usually applies to guides in books and "indices" is usually used in mathematics. Some nouns have irregular plurals in that the plural form and the singular form are the same. These include "sheep," "grouse" (the game bird), and "salmon." Some nouns have a regular plural and an irregular plural form. Thus "brother" has the plural forms "brothers" and "brethren," although "brethren" is now mainly used in a religious context and is archaic in general English.

irregular sentence *see* **major sentence**.

irregular verb

A verb that does not conform to the usual pattern of verbs in that some of its forms deviate from what one would expect if the pattern of regular verbs was being followed.

There are four main forms of a **regular verb**—the INFINITIVE or base form, as in "hint," "halt," "hate," and "haul"; the third person singular form, as "hints," "halts," "hates," and "hauls"; the -ING form or present participle, as "hinting," "halting," "hating," and "hauling";

the *-ed* form or "past tense" or "past participle," as "hinted," "halted," "hated," and "hauled."

Irregular verbs deviate in some way from that pattern, in particular from the pattern of adding *-ed* to the past tense and past participle. They fall into several categories.

One category concerns those that have the same form in the past tense and past participle forms as the infinitive and do not end in *-ed*, like regular verbs. These include:

infinitive	past tense	past participle
bet	bet	bet
burst	burst	burst
cast	cast	cast
cost	cost	cost
cut	cut	cut
hit	hit	hit
hurt	hurt	hurt
let	let	let
put	put	put
run	run	run
set	set	set
shed	shed	shed
shut	shut	shut
slit	slit	slit
split	split	split
spread	spread	spread

Some irregular verbs have two past tenses and two past participles that are the same. These include:

infinitive	past tense	past participle
burn	burned, burnt	burned, burnt,
hang	hanged, hung	hanged, hung
kneel	knelt, kneeled	knelt, kneeled
lean	leaned, lent	leaned, lent
leap	leaped, leapt	leaped, leapt
learn	learned, learnt	learned, learnt
light	lighted, lit	lighted, lit
smell	smelled, smelt	smelled, smelt
speed	speeded, sped	speeded, sped

infinitive	*past tense*	*past participle*
spill	spilled, spilt	spilled, spilt
spoil	spoiled, spoilt	spoiled, spoilt
wet	wetted, wet	wetted, wet

Some irregular verbs have past tenses that do not end in *-ed* and have the same form as the past participle. These include:

infinitive	*past tense*	*past participle*
bend	bent	bent
bleed	bled	bled
breed	bred	bred
build	built	built
cling	clung	clung
dig	dug	dug
feel	felt	felt
fight	fought	fought
find	found	found
flee	fled	fled
fling	flung	flung
grind	ground	ground
hear	heard	heard
hold	held	held
keep	kept	kept
lay	laid	laid
lead	led	led
leave	left	left
lend	lent	lent
lose	lost	lost
make	made	made
mean	meant	meant
meet	met	met
pay	paid	paid
rend	rent	rent
say	said	said
seek	sought	sought
sell	sold	sold
send	sent	sent
shine	shone	shone

infinitive	past tense	past participle
shoe	shod	shod
sit	sat	sat
sleep	slept	slept
slide	slid	slid
sling	slung	slung
slink	slunk	slunk
spend	spent	spent
spin	spun	spun
stand	stood	stood
stick	stuck	stuck
sting	stung	stung
strike	struck	struck
string	strung	strung
sweep	swept	swept
swing	swung	swung
teach	taught	taught
tell	told	told
think	thought	thought
understand	understood	understood
weep	wept	wept
win	won	won
wring	wrung	wrung

Some irregular verbs have regular past tense forms but two possible past participles, one of which is regular. These include:

infinitive	past tense	past participle
mow	mowed	mowed, mown
prove	proved	proved, proven
sew	sewed	sewn, sewed
show	showed	showed, shown
sow	sowed	sowed, sown
swell	swelled	swelled, swollen

Some irregular verbs have past tenses and past participles that are different from each other and different from the infinitive. These include:

infinitive	*past tense*	*past participle*
arise	arose	arisen
awake	awoke	awoken
bear	bore	borne
begin	began	begun
bid	bade	bidden
bite	bit	bitten
blow	blew	blown
break	broke	broken
choose	chose	chosen
do	did	done
draw	drew	drawn
drink	drank	drunk
drive	drove	driven
eat	ate	eaten
fall	fell	fallen
fly	flew	flown
forbear	forbore	forborne
forbid	forbade	forbidden
forgive	forgave	forgiven
forget	forgot	forgotten
forsake	forsook	forsaken
freeze	froze	frozen
forswear	forswore	foresworn
get	got	gotten
give	gave	given
go	went	gone
grow	grew	grown
hew	hewed	hewn
hide	hid	hidden
know	knew	known
lie	lay	lain
ride	rode	ridden
ring	rang	rung
saw	sawed	sawn
see	saw	seen
rise	rose	risen
shake	shook	shaken
shrink	shrank	shrunk

infinitive	*past tense*	*past participle*
slay	slew	slain
speak	spoke	spoken
spring	sprang	sprung
steal	stole	stolen
stink	stank	stunk
stride	strode	stridden
strive	strove	striven
swear	swore	sworn
swim	swam	swum
take	took	taken
tear	tore	torn
throw	threw	thrown
tread	trod	trodden
wake	woke	woken
wear	wore	worn
write	wrote	written

-ise *see* -ize.

-ish

A suffix indicating "somewhat," as in baldish, biggish, smallish, youngish, or "nationality," as in Spanish, Turkish, Polish.

-ism

A suffix indicating "state, condition," as in absenteeism, alcoholism, fatalism, heroism, plagiarism, or indicating "doctrine, movement, system, theory," as in Catholicism, Marxism, Reaganism. It now also indicates "discrimination," as in ageism, sexism, racism.

iso-

A prefix indicating "equal," as in isobar, isotherm, isosceles.

-ist

A suffix indicating "believer, supporter, practitioner," as in atheist, fascist, feminist, Methodist, or "discriminating against," as in ageist, sexist, racist.

italic type

A sloping typeface that is used for a variety of purposes. It is used to differentiate a piece of text from the main text, which is usually in Roman type. For example, it is used sometimes for the titles of books, newspapers, magazines, plays, movies, musical works, and works of art, as in "He is a regular reader of the *New York Times*," "She reads *National Geographic Magazine*," "Have you read *Animal Farm* by George Orwell?", "He has never seen a production of Shakespeare's *Othello*," "We went to hear Handel's *Messiah*," "*Mona Lisa* is a famous painting." Sometimes such titles are put in quotation marks rather than in italic.

Italic type is also sometimes used for the names of ships, trains, etc., as in "She once sailed in the *Queen Mary*" and "Their train was called *The Flying Scotsman*."

Italic type is also used for the Latin names of plants and animals, as in "of the genus *Lilium*," "trees of the genus *Pyrus*," "*Panthera pardus*," and "*Canis lupus*."

Italic type is sometimes used for foreign words that have been adopted into the English language but have never been fully integrated. Examples include *bête noire*, *raison d'être*, *inter alia*, and *Weltschmerz*.

Italic type can also sometimes be used to draw attention to a particular word, phrase, or passage, as in "How do you pronounce *formidable*?", or to emphasize a word or phrase, as in "Is he *still* in the same job?"

-ite

A suffix that meaning "believer, supporter, practitioner," as in Reaganite and Trotskyite.

-itis

A suffix meaning "illness or disease," as in bronchitis, hepatitis, meningitis.

its *and* it's

These are liable to be confused. **Its** is an adjective meaning "belonging to it," as in "The house has lost its charm" and "The dog does not like its kennel." **It's** means "it is," as in "Do you know if it's raining?" and "It's not fair to expect her to do all the house-work."

-ize *and* -ise

These are both verb endings. There are many verbs that are spelt ending in **-ize** in American English and can be spelt ending in either **-ize** or **-ise** in British English, as "computerize/ise," "economize/ise," "finalize/ise," "hospitalize/ise," "modernize/ise," "organize/ise," "realize/ise," "theorize/ise." There are a few verbs which cannot be spelt -ize. These include "advertise," "advise," "comprise," "despise," "exercise," "revise," "supervise," and "televise."

J

jargon

A technical or specialist language used among members of a particular profession or area. It is often used as a derogatory term to describe unnecessarily obscure or pretentious language, used within a profession, that is incomprehensible to members of the public who might come into contact with it and require to know what is being talked about. Jargon should be avoided in any document or situation involving lay people who have no specialist knowledge of the subject being referred to or of the language associated with it. Jargon in some professions easily becomes GOBBLEDYGOOK.

journalese

A derogatory name for the style of writing and choice of vocabulary supposedly found in newspapers. It is usually the style of writing in tabloid newspapers, such as widespread use of clichés, sensational language, and short sentences, that is meant by the term. *See* HEADLINE.

jussive

A type of clause or sentence that expresses a command, as in "Will you be quiet! I'm trying to study," "Let's not bother going to the party. I'm too tired," "Would you pass me that book," and "Look at that, everybody! The river broke its banks."

just

An adverb that indicates that something happened a short time previously. In British English it is usually used with the perfect tense of the verb that it accompanies, as in "I have just finished work," "We have just decided to buy a new car," "You've just missed the bus" and "She's just passed her driving test."

In American English, just usually accompanies the past tense of the verb, and sometimes in British English, especially in an informal context, as in "I just saw a bad accident on the freeway," "We just noticed that it's snowing," and "He just left."

Just has more than one meaning. It can also mean "only" and "exactly." In the sense of "only," care should be taken to position it in the correct place in the sentence. For example, in the sentence "He drank just two glasses of wine," it means that he drank only two glasses of wine, but in the sentence "He just drank two glasses of wine" it means that he very recently drank two glasses of wine. To add to the confusion, although people may be careful about the positioning of just in formal writing they tend not to be in informal writing or speech. Thus someone could say in reply to the questions "How much has he had to drink? Is he fit to drive?", "He just had two glasses of wine," meaning that that was all he had drunk. In speech the meaning is usually obvious from intonation and context.

Just can also be used in the sense of "only" in such sentences as "Just Peter went on vacation with his parents. The other children stayed at home" and "Just one coat was left. The rest were sold early on." Again, care should be taken to place just before the word it refers to in order to avoid ambiguity.

Just can also mean "exactly," as in "I see you have a food processor. That's just what I need," and "Where did you find that cape? That's just what I've been looking for."

K

kibbutzim

An example of an IRREGULAR PLURAL form. Most nouns in English form plurals by adding -s or -es to the singular form, as in "book and books" and "church and churches." However several words of foreign origin which have been adopted into English but not fully integrated retain the plural form found in the foreign language. "Kibbutz," meaning a communal settlement in Israel, is one such word. Of Hebrew origin, it retains the plural form kibbutzim. In some cases there is a growing tendency for foreign plurals to be anglicized, or to exist alongside an anglicized plural, as in "thesauruses/thesauri," but this is not yet the case with kibbutzim.

kilo-

A prefix indicating "a thousand," as in kilogram, kilohertz, kiloliter, kilometer, kilowatt.

-kin

A suffix indicating a diminutive or smaller form of something, as in lambkin, mannikin.

kind

A noun that can cause grammatical problems. It is used to refer to a class of people or things. Since it is a COUNT NOUN, it should take the plural form "kinds" after words such as "all" and "many," as in "He met all kinds of people when he was traveling around the world," "We found all kinds of treasure when we were clearing out the attic," and "We found all kinds of wild flower in the meadows." A singular noun should follow "kinds of," as in "We found all kinds of treasure," but it is quite common for people to use a plural noun instead, as in "We found all kinds of treasures." This is best restricted to informal or spoken use.

"These" and "those" are frequently found preceding **kind of**, as in "She doesn't like these kind of cakes" and "My mother used to make those kind of cookies" but this is incorrect, and "this" and "that" should be used, as in "I don't like that kind of joke" and "My mother prefers this kind of vacation."

The use of kind of to mean "somewhat" or "rather," as in "I'm kind of hungry," "She's kind of rude to him," and "It's kind of cold in here," should be restricted to informal speech or dialect. This phrase is sometimes written "kinda," as in "We're kinda bored."

Kind is also used as an adjective meaning "caring" or "generous," as in "A kind old lady lent the children money for the bus ride home," "It was kind of you to let them borrow your car," and "Children should be taught to be kind to animals."

-kind

A suffix meaning "a group of people," as in humankind, mankind, womankind.

kindly

A word that looks like an adverb but can be either an adverb or an adjective. As an adverb it means "in a kind or caring manner" or "generously," as in "They treated us kindly during our stay," "Her parents kindly treated us to a meal in a restaurant" and "They very kindly offered us a lift." The adverb kindly is also used in rather an ironic way when the user is annoyed, as in "Would you kindly stop allowing your dog to foul the pavement." It is also used in the phrase "not to take kindly to," meaning "to be unwilling to accept," as in "The new student doesn't take kindly to discipline," "He won't take kindly to being kept waiting" and "The candidate was so confident that he is unlikely to take kindly to being rejected."

Kindly is more common as an adjective and means "kind, warm, friendly," as in "a kindly old man who was always helping his neighbors" and "She gave the children a kindly smile."

kneel

One of several verbs in English that have more than one past participle and past tense form. The past participle and past tense can both be "kneeled" or "knelt," as in "The child knelt in prayer," "She kneeled before the altar," "She had knelt at her dying husband's bedside every night," and "They had kneeled in supplication before the emperor but he spurned them." Although both "knelt" and "kneeled" are acceptable, "knelt" is by far the more common form.

L

laid *and* lain

Words that are liable to be confused. **Laid** is the past tense and past participle of the verb "lay," meaning "to place or put," as in "She laid the antique vase carefully on the table," "He laid the new carpet in the den," "They have laid the baby on a mat on the floor," and "We have laid tiles on the kitchen floor." **Lain** is the past participle of the verb "lie," meaning "to rest in a horizontal position," as in "Those letters have lain on his desk all week," "The dead man had lain in the empty house for several days," and "They had lain on the beach in the midday sun."

language

The means by which human beings communicate using words, as in "Children acquire language at different rates. Some speak much earlier than others." Language can refer either to spoken or written communication. It can also refer to the variety of communication used by a particular nation or state, as in "He visits France regularly but makes no attempt to understand the French language," "Everyone should learn at least one foreign language," and "People in other parts of Europe tend to speak more languages than the British." The language that a person speaks from birth is known as his/her "first language" or "native language." He/she is said to be a native speaker of this language.

Language can also be used to refer to the style and vocabulary of a piece of writing, as in "The language of his novels is very poetic."

Language can also apply to the particular style and variety of language that is used in a particular profession or among a particular group of people with some common interest, as in "legal language," "scientific language," or "technical language." Such technical or specialist language is sometimes referred to rather pejoratively as JARGON or as "legalese," "medicalese," "computerese," etc.

A person's own style of language with regard to vocabulary, structure, etc., is known as IDIOLECT, as in "He is the son of academic parents and has rather a formal idiolect."

The language of a region or community with regard to vocabulary, structure, grammar and pronunciation is known as DIALECT, as in "the dialects of the Southern states of the US," "the dialect of the North of England,"

last

A word that can be an adverb or an adjective. As an adjective it can give rise to ambiguity. It can mean "coming after all others, final," as in "He was the last runner to hit the finishing tape," "That was the last novel he wrote before he died," "He did not die until he was 90 but he wrote his last novel at the age of 40." Ambiguity arises when last takes on other meanings. For example, it is frequently used as a synonym for "latest," as in "I really enjoyed his last novel and I'm looking forward to the next." In this particular sentence it is clear that last means "latest" not "final" but this is not always the case. For example, in the sentence "He was 60 when he directed his last movie," it is not at all clear from the evidence of the sentence alone whether it is his "final" or "latest" movie that is being referred to. Thus it is better to use either "final" or "latest" rather than "last" in order to clarify the meaning.

Confusion can arise also between last, meaning "final," and last, meaning "preceding," as in "I did not quite understand the last chapter." On the evidence of the sentence alone, it is not clear whether last refers to the preceding chapter or to the final chapter. Again it is best to avoid ambiguity by using a synonym for last.

Yet more confusion can be caused with regard to last when it is used to refer to days of the week. It varies from person to person whether "last Saturday" refers to the Saturday that has just gone or to the one before that. To some extent it depends which day of the week it is when the statement is made. To avoid ambiguity it is best to specify the date.

Last is also used as an adverb, as in "They last saw their father when he was going to war," "When the family go to the dentist my brother always wants to go in last," and "If you are adding cream to the soup you add it last." The adverbial use does not suffer from problems of ambiguity.

latest

An adjective that is liable to be confused with LAST. It can also mean "most up-to-date," "most fashionable," as in "the very latest dresses from the Paris designers." Latest is also found in this meaning in the phrase "the very latest," as in "She always dresses in the very latest." It can also mean "most late," the superlative of "late," in the sense of "far on in the day or night," as in "The latest train that you can get from that station leaves at ten o'clock." In this sense latest is also found in the phrase "at the latest" and in the phrase "at the very latest," meaning "most late time," as in "You must arrive at the station at ten o'clock at the latest" and "The students' papers must be handed in by Friday at the very latest."

lay *and* lie

These are liable to be confused. This is because **lay,** as well as being a verb in its own right, is also one of the principal parts of **lie**—the past tense, as in "They lay on the beach in the sun," "The books lay on the table gathering dust," and "She lay on her bed and wept."

Lay is a TRANSITIVE VERB meaning "to place or put," as in "She asked him to lay new tiles in the kitchen" and "She had to lay down her bags to open the door." The principal parts of lay are "lays" (third person singular present), as in "She always lays the baby on the grass to play"; "laying" (present participle), as in "Laying her bags down, she put her key in the lock"; "laid" (past participle and past tense), as in "She laid the package on the table" and "He had laid his car keys on the table and forgot about them."

Lie is an INTRANSITIVE VERB whose principal parts are "lies" (third person singular present), as in "Their house lies to the north of the village"; "lying" (present participle), as in "Lying on the grass, they looked up at the sky"; "lay" (past tense), as in "The climbers lay on the summit exhausted"; "lain" (past participle), as in "Those books have lain there for weeks."

Lie has another totally unrelated meaning. It means "to say or write something that is untrue," as in "You didn't have to lie about your part in the affair." The principal parts of the verb lie are "lies" (third person singular present), as in "he lies about why he arrives home late from work"; "lying" (present participle), as in "Lying, he looked her straight in the face"; "lied" (past participle and past tense), as in "He lied to his employers about his qualifications" and "She suddenly realized that he had lied all the time."

lean

One of several verbs in English that have two forms of the past tense and the past participle, "leaned" and "leant," as in "She leaned over the fence to talk to her neighbor," "He leaned over his desk to catch the attention of his co-workers," "They have leaned over backwards to help her," and "She has leant down to pick something up and hurt her back." Although both forms exist, "leant" is becoming obsolete in American English.

leap

One of several verbs in English that have two forms of the past tense and past participle, "leaped" and "leapt," as in "The children leaped around the park in high spirits," "She leapt up in surprise when she heard the news," "She had leaped over a high fence and broken her leg," and "The child has leapt over the stream and run off." The two forms are virtually interchangeable but "leaped" is slightly more common in American English.

learn

One of several verbs in English that have two forms of the past tense and past participle, "learned" and "learnt," as in "They learned French at school," "She learnt to ski in Austria," "I think the boys have learned their lesson," and "He had learnt to be grateful for what he was given." Although both forms are interchangeable in British English, the use of "learnt" in American English is regarded as an affectation. "Learned" as a past tense or past participle should not be confused with "learned," the adjective meaning "erudite, well-read, intellectual," as in "Students filled the lecture hall to listen to the learned professor" and "The firm publishes learned journals." This adjective is pronounced with two syllables—*ler-nid*—whereas "learned," the past tense and past participle, is pronounced as one syllable—*lernd*.

length mark

A mark used in phonetics in relation to a vowel to indicate that it is long. This can take the form of a "macron," a small horizontal stroke placed above a letter, or a symbol resembling a colon placed after a vowel in the IPA pronunciation system.

less *and* fewer

Two words that are liable to be confused. *See* FEWER.

-less

A suffix meaning "without or lacking," added to nouns to form adjectives, as in characterless, clueless, expressionless, fearless, flawless, harmless, homeless, hopeless, passionless, toothless, and useless. It can also mean "without being able to be measured," as in ageless, countless, priceless, and timeless.

-let

A suffix indicating a diminutive or smaller form of something, as in booklet, coverlet, droplet, islet, piglet, starlet, and streamlet.

letter-writing

This has become something of a dying art in view of the widespread use of the telephone and e-mail. However, all of us from time to time have to write some form of letter and many of these are business letters. There are a few conventions in formal letters that should be observed.

One's own address, including the zip code, should be placed at the right-hand side of the page. Each line of one's own address should be below the one above and the date put below the last line of the address, as in:

23 Park Drive
Meadowbrook
PA 19046

June 5, 2001

Whether one puts a comma at the end of the various lines of the address is a matter of taste. It is becoming common in modern usage not to do so. Note that there should be no period after the zip code.

One's telephone number can either be placed between the zip code and the date or at the other side of the page on the same line as the first line of the address.

If one is writing a business letter one should also put the address of the person to whom one is writing. It should be placed at the other side of the page below one's own address and the lines of this should be placed directly below each other without being indented, as in:

23 Park Drive
Meadowbrook
PA 19046

June 5, 2001

The Manager Eastlands Bank
333 West Street
Doylestown
PA 18901

With regard to deciding how to address the person to whom one is writing, it is best to find out his/her name. Having done so then one can start the letter off, as in:

Dear Mr White,

If one is writing to a woman the situation is slightly more problematic. Formerly it was considered acceptable to address the person written to as "Miss" if one knew her to be unmarried or as "Mrs" if one knew her to be married. If one did not know her marital status one could either use "Miss" or use the "Madam" convention. In modern usage "Ms" is the acceptable term if one does not know the marital status of the woman to whom one is writing. Many people prefer to use this designation even if they do know the person's marital status and many women prefer to be addressed in this way. On the other hand, some women, especially older women, do not like the "Ms" designation.

In modern usage some people prefer to put the first name and surname of the relevant person instead of the surname preceded by Mr, etc., as in:

Dear John White,

The above style of address is considered rather informal by some people.

If it is not easy to ascertain the name of the person to whom one wishes to write, then it is perfectly acceptable to address him/her in terms of their position or job, as in:

Dear manager,
Dear HR Manager,
Dear Area Manager,

In formal letters it is also acceptable to use "Sir" or "Madam," as in:

Dear Sir,
Dear Madam,
Dear Sir/Madam,

Obviously the above style of address is used in cases where one does not know the sex of the person to whom one is writing.

In ending a formal letter it was traditionally the custom to write "Yours faithfully" before one's signature, if one had addressed the person written to as "Dear Sir" or "Dear Madam," as in:

Yours faithfully
Jane Goldberg

It was also the custom to end the letter with "Yours sincerely" if the letter was either informal in nature or a formal letter which began with "Dear Mr White" etc., as in:

Yours sincerely,
Louise Grant

In modern usage it is now considered acceptable to end a letter with "Yours sincerely" even if one has begun it with "Dear Sir," etc. These days "Yours faithfully" is considered to be exceptionally formal. It is common to end even business letters with "Kind regards," especially if one knows the person being written to.

On the envelope the lines can be indented or not, according to taste. Each line, except the last one, can have a comma after or not.

However, in modern usage there is an increasing tendency to punctuate as little as possible and the commas are frequently omitted, as in:

Ms Mary Brown
29 Lower Forth Street
Meadowbrook
PA 19046

The same comments on Mrs, Miss, and Ms apply to envelopes as apply to the opening greeting in letters. *See above.* In modern usage it is becoming increasingly common to write the full name of the person written to on the envelope, as in:

James Black
36 High Street
Sayville
NY 19087

It is considered formal or old-fashioned to use "Esq.," usually spelt with a period at the end and preceded by a comma. If used, "Esq." should be placed after the man's name and there should be no accompanying "Mr," as in:

John Brown, Esq.
43 Queen Street
Stonybrook
NY 19078

lexicography
The art and practice of defining words, selecting them, and arranging them in dictionaries and glossaries.

lie *see* lay.

ligature
A printed character combining two letters in one, as in æ and œ. It is sometimes called a DIGRAPH.

-like

A suffix indicating similarity, as in childlike, cowlike, dreamlike, ladylike, lifelike, warlike.

limerick

A humorous five-lined piece of light verse, with the first two lines rhyming with each other, the third and fourth lines rhyming with each other, and the fifth line rhyming with the first line. Usually there are three stressed beats in the first, second, and fifth lines and two stressed beats on the third and fourth lines. Traditionally the name of a place is mentioned in the first line and may be repeated in the last line. Edward Lear made the form popular in the nineteenth century. Limerick is a town in Ireland but the name of the verse is probably derived from a Victorian custom of singing nonsense songs at parties where "Will you come up to Limerick?" was a common refrain. An example is:

> There once was a man from Nantucket
> Who kept all his cash in a bucket;
> But his daughter named Nan
> Ran away with a man,
> And as for the bucket, Nantucket.

line-break

The division of a word at the end of a line for space purposes. This is marked by a HYPHEN.

-ling

A suffix indicating a diminutive or smaller version of something, as in duckling, gosling, nestling.

lingua franca

A language defined as "a language adopted as a common language by speakers whose native languages are different." This enables people to have a common medium of communication for various purposes, such as trading. Examples include Swahili in East Africa, Hausa in West Africa and Tok Pisin in Papua New Guinea. The term historically referred to "a language that was a mixture of Italian, French, Greek, Spanish, and Arabic, used for trading and military purposes."

linguistics

The systematic scientific study of language. It describes language and seeks to establish general principles rather than to prescribe rules of correctness.

linking adverbs

Words and phrases that indicate some kind of connection between one clause or sentence and another. Examples include "however," as in "The award had no effect on their financial situation. It did, however, have a marked effect on their morale"; "moreover," as in "He is an unruly student. Moreover, he is a bad influence on the other students"; "then again," as in "She does not have very good qualifications. Then again, most of the other candidates have even fewer"; "in the meantime," as in "We will not know the planning committee's decision until next week. In the meantime we can only hope"; "instead," as in "I thought he would have resigned. Instead he seems determined to stay."

linking verb

A verb that "links" a subject with its complement. Unlike other verbs, linking verbs do not denote an action but indicate a state. Examples of linking verbs include "He is a fool," "She appears calm," "He appeared a sensible man," "You seemed to become anxious," "They became Buddhists," "The child feels unwell," "It is getting rather warm," "It is growing colder," "You look well," "She remained loyal to her friend," "She lived in the US but remained a British citizen," "You seem thoughtful," and "She seems a nice person." Linking verbs are also called **copulas** or **copular verbs**.

literary criticism

The formal study, discussion, and evaluation of a literary work, as in "The students who are studying literary criticism have been asked to write a critical analysis of *Ulysses* by James Joyce."

litotes

A kind of understatement in which a statement is conveyed by contradicting or denying its opposite, as in "It will be no easy task to look after their children for a week" (meaning that it will be a difficult task), "She's not exactly communicative" (meaning she is silent or reserved).

loan word

A word that has been taken into one language from another. From the point of view of the language taking the word in, the word is known as a BORROWING. Some loan words become naturalized or fully integrated into the language and have a pronunciation and spelling reflecting the conventions of the language that has borrowed it. Other loan words retain the spelling and pronunciation of the language from which they have been borrowed. These include "Gastarbeiter," borrowed from German and meaning "a foreign worker."

localism

A word or expression the use of which is restricted to a particular place or area. The area in question can be quite small, unlike DIALECT words or "regionalism."

-log

A suffix derived from Greek indicating conversation or discussion, as in dialog, epilog, monolog, prolog, travelog.

lower-case letter

The opposite of CAPITAL LETTER. It is also known informally as "small letter." Lower-case letters are used for most words in the language. It is capital letters that are exceptional in their use.

-ly

A common adverbial ending. See ADVERBS.

M

macro-

A prefix derived from the Greek meaning "large in size or scope," as in macrobiotic, macrocosm, macroeconomics, macromolecular, macrostructure.

macron *see* **length mark**.

main clause

The principal clause in a sentence, on which any SUBORDINATE CLAUSES depend for their sense. The main clause can stand alone and make some sense but the subordinate clauses cannot. In the sentence "I left early because I wanted to catch the 6 o'clock train," "I left early" is the main clause and "because I wanted to catch the 6 o'clock train" is the subordinate clause. In the sentence "When we saw the strange man we were afraid," the main clause is "we were afraid" and the subordinate clause is "when we saw the strange man." In the sentence "Because it was late we decided to start out for home as soon as we could," the main clause is "we decided to start out for home" and the subordinate clauses are "because it was late" and "as soon as we could." A main clause can also be known as a **principal clause** or an INDEPENDENT CLAUSE.

major sentence

A sentence that contains at least one SUBJECT and a FINITE VERB, as in "We are going" and "They won." They frequently have more elements than this, as in "They bought a car," "We lost the game," "They arrived yesterday," and "We are going away next week." They are sometimes described as **regular** because they divide into certain structural patterns: a subject, finite verb, adverb, or adverbial clause, etc. The opposite of a major sentence is called a **minor sentence**, **irregular sentence**, or **fragmentary sentence**. These include interjections such as "Ouch!" and "How terrible"; formula expressions, such as "Good morning" and "Well done"; and short forms of longer expressions, as in "Traffic diverted," "Store closed," "No dogs," and "Flooding ahead." Such short forms could be rephrased to become major sentences, as in "Traffic has been diverted because of highway construction," "The store is closed on Sundays," "The owner does not allow dogs in the store," and "There was flooding ahead on the freeway."

mal-

A prefix derived from French meaning "bad, unpleasant," as in malodorous, or "imperfect, faulty," as in malabsorption, maladjusted, maladministration, malformation, malfunctioning, malnutrition, malpractice, maltreatment.

malapropism

The incorrect use of a word, often through confusion with a similar-sounding word. It often arises from someone's attempt to impress someone else with a knowledge of long words or of technical language. Examples include "The doctor says the old man is not in possession of all his facilities." Here "facilities" has been wrongly used instead of "faculties." Another example is "My friend lives in a computer belt." Here "computer" has been wrongly used instead of "commuter." Another example is "Her husband's had a vivisection." Here "vivisection" has been used instead of "vasectomy." "Ah! It's wonderful to be on terracotta again. I hate sailing." Here "terracotta" has been wrongly used instead of "terra firma." The effect of malapropism is often humorous. Sometimes people use it deliberately for comic effect, as in "He was under the affluence of incahol."

Malapropism is called after Mrs Malaprop, a character in a play called *The Rivals* (1775), a comedy by R. B. Sheridan. Her name is derived from the French *mal à propos*, "not apposite, inappropriate." Some of her malapropisms in the play include "She's as headstrong as an allegory on the banks of the Nile." She has used "allegory" wrongly instead of "alligator." Another of Mrs Malaprop's malapropisms is "Illiterate him quite from your mind." Here she has used "illiterate" wrongly instead of "obliterate."

-man

A suffix used with nouns to form nouns indicating someone's job, as in barman, chairman, clergyman, fireman, mailman, policeman, salesman.

In modern usage, when attempts are being made to remove sexism from the language, alternatives have been sought for any words ending in -man. Formerly, words ending in -man were often used whether or not the person referred to was definitely known to be a man. Different ways have been found to avoid the sexism of -man. "Salesman" has been changed in many cases to "salesperson," "chairman" often becomes "chairperson" or "chair." Similarly, "fireman" has become "fire-fighter" and "policeman" frequently becomes "police officer." *See* -PERSON.

-mania

A suffix indicating abnormal or obsessional behavior, as in kleptomania, nymphomania, pyromania.

manner, adverbial clause of *see* adverbial clause.

manner, adverbs of *see* adverb.

masculine

In grammatical terms, one of the GENDERS that nouns are divided into. Nouns in the masculine gender include words that obviously belong to the male sex, as in "man," "boy," "king," "prince," "bridegroom," "schoolboy," and "mailman." Many words now considered to be of DUAL GENDER formerly were assumed to be masculine. These include such words as "author," "sculptor," and "engineer." Gender also applies to personal pronouns, and the third personal singular pronoun masculine is "he" (subject), "him" (object) and "his" (possessive). For further information *see* HE; SHE.

mass noun

A noun that is not usually pluralized or "counted." Such a noun is usually preceded by "some," rather than "a." Mass nouns often refer to substances, commodities, qualities, processes, and states. Examples of mass nouns include baggage, butter, china, gas, sugar, heat, information, poverty, richness, and warmth. In some situations it is possible to have a count version of what is usually a mass noun. Thus "sugar" is usually considered to be a mass noun but it can be used in a count form in contexts such as "I take two sugars in my coffee, please." Some nouns exist in a mass and count form. Examples include "cake," as in "Have some cake" and "She ate three cakes" and "light", as in "She could not paint for lack of light" and "The lights went out."

-mate

A suffix referring to "someone who shares something with someone," as in bedmate, classmate, roommate, schoolmate, shipmate, teammate.

mega-

A prefix derived from Greek meaning "very large," as in megabid, megabucks, megaproduction, and megastar. Many words using mega- in this way are modern and many are also informal or slang. In technical language mega-means "a million times bigger than the unit to which it is attached," as in megabyte, megacycle, megahertz, megawatt.

meiosis

A figure of speech using understatement to emphasize the size or importance of something, as in "He's a decent enough bloke" and "He's rather a decent tennis player."

melted *and* molten

Words that are liable to be confused. **Melted** is the past tense and past participle of the verb "to melt," as in "The chocolate melted in the heat" and "The ice cream had melted by the time they got home." Melted is also used as an adjective, as in "melted chocolate." **Molten** is used only as an adjective but it is not synonymous with melted. It means "melted or made liquid at high temperatures," as in "molten lava" and "molten metal."

meta-

A prefix derived from Greek meaning "alteration or transformation," as in metamorphosis, metaphor, metaphysics.

metaphor

A figure of speech that compares two things by saying that one thing is another, as in "He was a lion in the fight" (meaning that he was as brave as a lion), "She is a mouse whenever he is present" (meaning that she is very timid), "He is a giant among men" (meaning that he is a great man), "She was a shining light to us all" (meaning she was a source of inspiration), and "Life was not a bed of roses" (meaning life was not easy and enjoyable). By extension, metaphor refers to a word or phrase used in a sentence where it does not have a literal meaning, as in "a butter mountain," "a wine lake," "My co-worker is a snake in the grass," "She always sits on the fence at committee meetings," "They walked home with leaden feet," and "He was rooted to the spot when he saw the man with the gun." *See* MIXED METAPHOR and SIMILE.

-meter[1]

A suffix indicating "a measuring instrument," as in altimeter, barometer, calorimeter, pedometer, speedometer, thermometer.

-meter[2]

A suffix indicating "meter, the unit of length," as in centimeter, kilometer, and millimeter.

metonym

A figure of speech in which a word or expression is used to indicate something with which it has a close relationship, as in "The position of the Crown is more uncertain than it was formerly" (meaning that the position of the monarchy is not as stable as it once was), and "The Kremlin began to adopt a more enlightened approach to foreign visitors" (meaning that the Russian government began to adopt a more enlightened approach to foreign visitors), "The White House has yet to comment on the proposal" (meaning that the President of the United States has yet to reply to the proposal).

micro-

A prefix derived from Greek meaning "very small," as in microbiology, microfiche, microfilm, microscope, microsurgery.

milli-

A prefix derived from Latin meaning "thousand," as in millisecond, millennium.

mini-

A prefix derived from Latin meaning "very small, least," as in minimum, minimal, and miniature. Mini-is frequently used to form modern words, as in minibar, minibus, minicar, minicomputer, mini-cruise, mini-mall, miniskirt. Modern words beginning with mini- can be spelt either with a hyphen or without.

minor sentence *see* **major sentence**.

mis-

A prefix meaning "badly, wrongly," as in misbehave, miscalculate, misdirect, mishandle, mishear, misjudge, mismanage, mispronounce, misspell, mistreat, mistrust, misunderstanding, misuse.

misrelated participle *see* **dangling participle**.

mixed metaphor

The situation that occurs when unrelated METAPHORS are put in the same sentence. Examples include "She sailed into the room with both guns blazing." Here the use of the word "sail" belongs to nautical metaphors but the "guns blazing" belongs to cowboy or Western metaphors. Another example is "The company's new flagship did not get off the ground." Here "flagship" is a nautical term while "get off the ground" refers to an aircraft taking off. Another example is "They were caught red-handed with their pants down." Here "caught red-handed" is a metaphorical reference to a murderer caught with blood on his/her hands but "caught with one's pants down" is either a reference to the embarrassing experience of being caught unawares in the bathroom or else caught in an embarrassing sexual situation.

modal verb

A type of AUXILIARY VERB that "helps" the main verb to express a range of meanings including, for example, such meanings as possibility, probability, wants, wishes, necessity, permission, suggestions, etc. The main modal verbs are "can," "could"; "may," "might"; "will," "would"; "shall," "should"; "must." Modal verbs have only one form. They have no *-s* form in the third person singular, no infinitive, and no participles. Examples of modal verbs include "He cannot read or write," "She could go if she wanted to" (expressing ability); "You can have another cookie," "You may answer the question" (expressing permission); "We may see her on the way to the station," "We might get there by nightfall" (expressing possibility); "Will you have some wine?", "Would you take a seat?" (expressing an offer or invitation); "We should arrive by dawn," "That must be a record" (expressing probability and certainty); "You may prefer to wait," "You might like to leave instructions" (expressing suggestion); "Can you find the time to call him for me?", "Could you give him a message?" (expressing instructions and requests); "They must leave at once," "We must get there on time" (expressing necessity).

modifier

A word, or group of words, that "modifies" or affects the meaning of another word in some way, usually by adding more information about it. Modifiers are frequently used with nouns. They can be adjectives, as in "He works in the *main* building" and "They need a *larger* house." Modifiers of nouns can be nouns themselves, as in "the *theater* profession," "the *publishing* industry," and "*singing* tuition." They can also be place names, as in "the *Washington* train," "a *Paris* café" and "the *New York* subway," or adverbs of place and direction, as in "a *downstairs* bathroom" and "an *upstairs* living room."

Adverbs, adjectives, and pronouns can be accompanied by modifiers. Examples of modifiers with adverbs include "walking *amazingly* quickly" and "stopping *incredibly* abruptly." Examples of modifiers with adjectives include "a *really* hot day" and "a *deliriously* happy child." Examples of modifiers with pronouns include "*almost* no one there" and "*practically* everyone present."

The examples given above are all premodifiers. *See also* POST-MODIFIER.

molten *see* melted.

-monger

A suffix derived from Old English meaning "dealer, trader," as in fishmonger, ironmonger. As well as being used for occupations in which people sell things, it is used for people who "trade" in less tangible things, as in gossipmonger, newsmonger, rumormonger, scandalmonger, warmonger.

mono-

A prefix derived from Greek meaning "one, single," as in mono-chrome, monocracy, monogamy, monolog, monoplane, monosyl-labic, monoxide.

months of the year

These are spelt with initial capital letters, as January, February, March, April, May, June, July, August, September, October, November, December.

mood

One of the categories into which verbs are divided. The verb moods are indicative, imperative, and subjunctive.

The **indicative** makes a statement, as in "He lives in San Francisco," "They have two children," and "It's starting to rain." The **imperative** is used for giving orders or making requests, as in "Shut that door!", "Sit quietly until the teacher arrives," and "Please bring me some coffee." The **subjunctive** was originally a term in Latin grammar and expressed a wish, supposition, doubt, improbability, or other non-factual statement. It is used in English for hypothetical statements and certain formal "that" clauses, as in "If I were you I would have nothing to do with it," "If you were to go now you would arrive on time," "Someone suggested that we ask for more money," and "It was his lawyer who suggested that he sue the firm." The word "mood" arose because it was said to indi-cate the verb's attitude or viewpoint.

more

An adverb that is added to some adjectives to make the compara-tive form (*see* COMPARISON OF ADJECTIVES). In general it is the longer adjectives that have more as part of their comparative form, as in "more abundant," "more beautiful," "more catastrophic," "more dangerous," "more elegant," "more frantic," "more graceful," "more handsome," "more intelligent," "more luxurious," "more manageable," "more opulent," "more precious," "more ravishing," "more satisfactory," "more talented," "more unusual," "more valu-able." Examples of adverbs with more in their comparative form include "more elegantly," "more gracefully," "more energetically," "more dangerously," "more determinedly."

most

An adverb added to some adjectives and adverbs to make the superlative form. In general it is the longer adjectives that have most as part of their superlative form, as in "most abundant," "most beautiful," "most catastrophic," "most dangerous," "most elegant," "most frantic," "most graceful," "most handsome," "most intelligent," "most luxurious," "most manageable," "most noteworthy," "most opulent," "most precious," "most ravishing," "most satisfactory," "most talented," "most unusual," "most valuable." Examples of adverbs with most in their superlative form include "most elegantly," "most gracefully," "most energetically," "most dangerously" and "most determinedly."

mother tongue

The language that one first learns, the language of which he/she is a "native speaker." It means the same as "first language" or "native language."

Ms, Miss, *and* Mrs *see* letter-writing.

mow

A verb that has two possible past participles—"mowed" and "mown"—as in "He has not yet mowed the grass" and "We have mown the grass several times this summer." However, **mown** is now virtually restricted to adjectival uses, as in "the smell of freshly mown hay." Only **mowed** can be used as the past tense, as in "They mowed the grass yesterday" and "If they mowed the grass more often the garden would be tidier."

multi-

A prefix derived from Latin meaning "many," as in multiply, multitude, multitudinous. Multi- is frequently used to form new modern words, as in multi-married, multi-media, multi-publicized, multi-purpose, multi-story, multi-talented, multi-traveled.

multi-sentence

A sentence with more than one clause, as in "She tripped over a rock and broke her ankle" and "She was afraid when she saw the strange man."

N

-naut

A suffix derived from Greek meaning "sailor, navigator," as in astronaut, cosmonaut.

negative sentence

A sentence that is the opposite of a **positive sentence**. "She has a dog" is an example of a positive sentence. "She does not have a dog" is an example of a negative sentence. The negative concept is expressed by an AUXILIARY VERB accompanied by "not" or "n't." Other words used in negative sentences include "never," "nothing," and "by no means," as in "She has never been here" and "We heard nothing."

neither

An adjective or a pronoun that takes a singular verb, as in "Neither parent will come" and "Neither of them wishes to come." In the **neither ... nor** construction, a singular verb is used if both parts of the construction are singular, as in "Neither Donna nor Julia was present." If both parts are plural, the verb is plural, as in "Neither their parents nor their grandparents are willing to look after them." If the construction involves a mixture of singular and plural, the verb traditionally agrees with the subject that is nearest to it, as in "Neither her mother nor her grandparents are going to come" and "Neither her grandparents nor her mother is going to come." If pronouns are used, the nearer one governs the verb, as in "Neither they nor he is at fault" and "Neither he nor they are at fault."

neologism

A word that has been newly coined or newly introduced into the language, as "ecotourism," "hyperlink," and "videodisk."

neuro-

A prefix derived from Greek meaning "nerve," as in neuritis, neurology, neuron, neurosurgery.

neuter

One of the grammatical GENDERS. The other two grammatical genders are MASCULINE and FEMININE. Inanimate objects are members of the neuter gender. Examples include "table," "desk," "yard," "spade," "flower," and "bottle."

nominal clause *see* noun clause.

non-finite clause

A clause that contains a NON-FINITE VERB. Thus in the sentence "He works hard to earn a living," "to earn a living" is a non-finite clause since "to earn" is an infinitive and so a non-finite verb. Similarly, in the sentence "Getting there was a problem," "getting there" is a non-finite clause, "getting" being a present participle and so a non-finite verb.

non-finite verb

A verb that shows no variation in tense and has no subject. The non-finite verb forms include the infinitive form, as in "go," the present participle and gerund, as in "going," and the past participle, as in "gone."

non-gradable *see* gradable.

noun

The name of something or someone. Thus "anchor," "baker," "cat," "elephant," "foot," "gate," "lake," "pear," "shoe," "trunk," and "window" are all nouns. There are various categories of noun. *See* ABSTRACT NOUN, COMMON NOUN, CONCRETE NOUN, COUNT NOUN, MASS NOUN, and PROPER NOUN.

noun clause

A SUBORDINATE CLAUSE that performs a function in a sentence similar to a noun or noun phrase. It can act as the subject, object, or complement of a MAIN CLAUSE. In the sentence "Where he goes is his own business," "where he goes" is a noun clause. In the sentence "They asked why he objected," "why he objected" is a noun clause. A noun clause is also known as a **nominal clause**.

noun phrase

A group of words containing a noun as its main word and functioning like a noun in a sentence. Thus it can function as the SUBJECT, OBJECT, or COMPLEMENT of a sentence. In the sentence "The big black dog bit him," "the big black dog" is a noun phrase, and in the sentence "They bought a house with a backyard," "a house with a backyard" is a noun phrase. In the sentence "She is a complete fool," "a complete fool" is a noun phrase.

number

In grammar this is a classification consisting of "singular" and "plural." Thus the number of the pronoun "they" is "plural" and the number of the verb "carries" is singular. *See* NUMBER AGREEMENT.

number agreement *or* concord

The agreement of grammatical units in terms of NUMBER. Thus a singular subject is followed by a singular verb, as in "The girl likes flowers," "He hates work," and "She was carrying a suitcase." Similarly, a plural subject should be followed by a plural verb, as in "They have many problems," "The men work hard," and "The girls are training hard."

numbers

These can be written in either figures or words. It is largely a matter of taste which method is adopted. As long as the method is consistent it does not really matter. Some establishments, such as a publishing house or a newspaper office, will have a house style. For example, some of them prefer to have numbers up to ten written in words, as in "They have two boys and three girls." If this system is adopted, guidance should be sought as to whether a mixture of figures and words in the same sentence is acceptable, as in "We have 12 cups but only six saucers," or whether the rule should be broken in such situations as "We have twelve cups but only six saucers."

numeral

A word for "number," as in "Print all the numerals in bold type." Numeral is often used to refer to "one, two, three, etc." in grammar since NUMBER is used to refer to the singular/plural category.

O

object

The part of a sentence that is acted upon or is affected by the verb. It usually follows the verb to which it relates. There are two forms of object—the DIRECT OBJECT and the INDIRECT OBJECT.

A direct object can be a noun, and in the sentence "The girl hit the ball," "ball" is a noun and the object; in the sentence "They bought a house," "house" is a noun and the object; in the sentence "They made an error," "error" is a noun and the object.

A direct object can be a noun phrase, and in the sentence "He has bought a large house," "a large house" is a noun phrase and the object; in the sentence "She loves the little girl," "the little girl" is a noun phrase and the object; in the sentence "They both wear black clothes," "black clothes" is a noun phrase and the object.

A direct object can be a noun clause, and in the sentence "I know what he means," "what he means" is a noun phrase and the object; in the sentence "He denied that he had been involved," "that he had been involved" is a noun phrase and the object; in the sentence "I asked when he would return," "when he would return" is a noun phrase and the object.

A direct object can also be a pronoun, and in the sentence "She hit him," "him" is a pronoun and the object; in the sentence "They had a car but they sold it," "it" is a pronoun and the object; in the sentence "She loves them," "them" is a pronoun and the object.

objective case

The case expressing the OBJECT. In Latin it is known as the ACCUSATIVE.

oblique

A diagonal mark (/) that has various uses. Its principal use is to show alternatives, as in "he/she," "Dear Sir/Madam," "a two-/three-room apartment" and "the budget for 2001/2." The oblique is used in some abbreviations, as in "c/o Smith" (meaning "care of Smith").

The word "per" is usually shown by means of an oblique, as in 60 km/h (60 kilometers per hour).

officialese

A derogatory term for the vocabulary and style of writing often found in official reports and documents and thought of as being pretentious and difficult to understand. It is usually considered to be the prime example of GOBBLEDYGOOK.

-oholic *see* -aholic.

-ology

A suffix derived from Greek meaning "study of," as in biology, geology, technology.

omni-

A prefix derived from Latin meaning "all," as in omnipotent, omnivorous.

onomatopoeia

A figure of speech that uses words whose sound suggests their meaning, as in "The sausages sizzled in the frying pan," "The fire crackled in the grate," and "The water gurgled in the pipes."

ordinal numbers

The numbers "first," "second," "third," etc., as opposed to CARDINAL NUMBERS, which are "one," "two," "three," etc.

orthographic

A term that refers to spelling, as in "words which give rise to orthographic problems."

orthography

The study or science of how words are spelt, as in "Make a survey of the orthography and the pronunciation of Scandinavian languages."

-osis

A suffix derived from Greek meaning either "a disease," as in cirrhosis and thrombosis, or a "development," as in metamorphosis.

oxymoron

A figure of speech that is based on the linking of incongruous or contradictory words, as in "and honor rooted in dishonor stood" (Tennyson) and "the wisest fool in Christendom."

P

paragraph

A subdivision of a piece of prose. Many people find it difficult to divide their work into paragraphs. Learning to do so can be difficult but it is an area of style that improves with practice.

A paragraph should deal with one particular theme or point of the writer's writing or argument. When that has been dealt with, a new paragraph should be started. However, there are other considerations to be taken into account. If the paragraph is very long it can appear off-putting visually to the reader and can be difficult to make one's way through it. In such cases it is best to subdivide themes and shorten paragraphs. On the other hand, it is best not to make all one's paragraphs too short as this can create a disjointed effect. It is best to try to aim for a mixture of lengths to create some variety.

Traditionally it was frowned upon to have a one-sentence paragraph but there are no hard and fast rules about this. Usually it takes more than one sentence to develop the theme of the paragraph, unless one is a tabloid journalist or a copywriter for an advertising firm, and it is best to avoid long, complex sentences.

The opening paragraph of a piece of writing should introduce the topic about which one is writing. The closing paragraph should sum up what one has been writing about. New paragraphs begin on new lines and they are usually indented from the margin. In the case of dialog in a work of fiction, each speaker's utterance usually begins on a new line for the clarification of the reader.

parentheses

A pair of characters that are used to enclose information that is in some way additional to a main statement. The information so enclosed is called **parenthesis** and the pair of characters enclosing it are known as **parentheses**, or brackets. The information that is enclosed in the parentheses is purely supplementary or explanatory in nature and could be removed without changing the overall basic meaning or grammatical completeness of the statement. Parentheses, like commas and dashes, interrupt the flow of the main statement but parentheses indicate a more definite or clear-cut interruption. The fact that they are more visually obvious emphasizes this.

Material within parentheses can be one word, as in "In a local wine bar we had some delicious crepes (pancakes)" and "They didn't have the chutzpah (nerve) to challenge her." It can also take the form of dates, as in "Robert Louis Stevenson (1850–94) wrote *Treasure Island*" and "*Animal Farm* was written by George Orwell (1903–50)."

The material within parentheses can also take the form of a phrase, as in "They served lasagne (a kind of pasta) and some delicious veal" and "They were drinking Calvados (a kind of brandy made from apples)," or in the form of a clause, as in "We were to have supper (or so they called it) later in the evening" and "They went for a walk around the loch (as a lake is called in Scotland) before making their departure."

It can also take the form of a complete sentence, as in "He was determined (we don't know why) to tackle the problem alone" and "She made it clear (nothing could be more clear) that she was not interested in the offer." Sentences that appear in parentheses in the middle of a sentence are not usually given an initial capital letter or a period, as in "They very much desired (she had no idea why) to buy her house." If the material within parentheses comes at the end of a sentence the period comes outside the second parenthesis, as in "For some reason we agreed to visit her at home (we had no idea where she lived)."

If the material in the parentheses is a sentence that comes between two other sentences it is treated like a normal sentence with an initial capital letter and a closing period, as in "He never seems to do any studying. (He is always either asleep or watching TV.) Yet he does brilliantly in his tests." Punctuation of the main statement is unaffected by the presence of the parentheses and their enclosed material except that any punctuation that would have followed the word before the first parenthesis follows the second parenthesis, as in "He always calls me Elizabeth (I am not sure why), which is my middle name."

participle

A part of speech, so called because, although a verb, it has the character both of verb and adjective and is also used in the formation of some compound tenses. *See also* -ING WORDS and PAST PARTICIPLE.

parts of speech

The categories (e.g. verb, noun, adjective, etc.) into which words are divided according to their grammatical and semantic functions.

passive voice

The voice of a verb whereby the subject is the recipient of the action of the verb. Thus, in the sentence "Rachel was kicked by her brother," "Rachel" is the receiver of the "kick" and so "kick" is in the passive voice. Had it been in the active voice it would have been "Her brother kicked Rachel." Thus "her brother" is the subject and not the receiver of the action.

past participle

This is formed by adding -*ed* or -*d* to the base words of regular verbs, as in "acted," "alluded," "boarded," "dashed," "flouted," "handed," "loathed," "tended," and "wanted," or in various other ways for IRREGULAR VERBS.

past tense

This TENSE of a verb is formed by adding -*ed* or -*d* to the base form of the verb in regular verbs, as in "added," "crashed," "graded," "smiled," "rested," and "yielded," and in various ways for IRREGULAR VERBS.

perfect tense *see* **tense**.

period

A punctuation mark consisting of a small dot (.). Its principal use is to end a sentence that is not a question or an exclamation, as in "They spent all the money." "She is studying hard." "He has been laid off and is very upset." "Because she is bashful, she rarely goes to parties."

The period is also used in decimal fractions, as in "4.5 meters," "6.3 miles," and "12.2 liters," and in dates, as in "2.22.01."

In modern usage the tendency is to omit periods from abbreviations. This is most true of abbreviations involving initial capital letters as in ATM, CIA, NAACP, and PGA. In such cases periods should definitely not be used if one or some of the initial letters do not belong to a full word. Thus, television is abbreviated to TV and monosodium glutamate to MSG.

There are usually no periods in abbreviations involving the first and last letters of a word (contractions), as in Dr, Mr, Rd, St, but this is a matter of taste.

Abbreviations involving the first few letters of a word, as in "Prof." (Professor) are the most likely to have periods, as in "Feb." (February), but again this is now a matter of taste.

For the use of the period in direct speech *see* DIRECT SPEECH. The period can also be called a **full stop**.

personal pronoun

A pronoun that is used to refer back to someone or something that has already been mentioned. The personal pronouns are divided into subject pronouns, object pronouns, and possessive pronouns. They are also categorized according to "person." *See* FIRST PERSON, SECOND PERSON, and THIRD PERSON.

personification

A form of METAPHOR that represents an inanimate object or abstract notion as possessing the attributes of a person. For example, Uncle Sam is a personification of the USA, while John Bull is a personification of England.

philology

The science, especially comparative, of languages and their history and structure.

phonetics

The science connected with pronunciation and the representation of speech sounds.

phrasal verb

A usually simple verb that combines with a preposition or adverb, or both, to convey a meaning more than the sum of its parts, e.g. to phase out, to come out, to look forward to.

phrase

Two or more words, usually not containing a FINITE VERB, that form a complete expression by themselves or constitute a portion of a sentence.

plural noun

The form of a noun referring to "more than one" and contrasted with a SINGULAR NOUN. Singular nouns form plural forms in different ways. Most singular nouns add *s*, as in "bat/bats," "monkey/ monkeys," "table/tables," "umbrella/umbrellas," or add *es*, as in "church/churches," "torch/torches." Singular nouns ending in a consonant followed by *y* add *ies*, as in "fairy/fairies" and "story/ stories." Some plural forms are formed irregularly (*see* IRREGULAR PLURALS). Some nouns are encountered in their plural form only. These include pants, scissors, and vermin.

positive sentence *see* negative sentence.

possessive apostrophe *see* apostrophe².

possessive pronoun *see* personal pronoun, first person, second person, third person.

postmodifier

A MODIFIER that comes after the main word of a NOUN PHRASE, as in "of stone" in "tablets of stone."

predicate

All the parts of a clause or sentence that are not contained in the subject. Thus in the sentence "The little girl was exhausted and hungry," "exhausted and hungry" is the predicate. Similarly, in the sentence "The tired old man slept like a baby," "slept like a baby" is the predicate.

predicative adjective

An adjective that helps to form the PREDICATE and so comes after the verb, as "tired" in "She was very tired" and "mournful" in "The music was very mournful."

prefix *see* affix.

premodifier

A MODIFIER that comes before the main word of a NOUN PHRASE, as "green" in "green dress" and "pretty" in "pretty houses."

preposition

A word that relates two elements of a sentence, clause, or phrase together. Prepositions show how the elements relate in time or space and generally precede the words that they "govern." Words governed by prepositions are nouns or pronouns. Prepositions are often very short words, as "at," "in," "on," "to," "before," and "after." Some complex prepositions consist of two words, as "ahead of," "instead of," "apart from," and some consist of three, as "with reference to," "in accordance with," and "in addition to." Examples of prepositions in sentences include "The cat sat on the mat," "We were at a concert," "They are in shock," "We are going to Florida," "She arrived before me," "Apart from you she has no friends," and "We acted in accordance with your instructions."

present continuous *see* tense.

present participle *see* -ing words.

present tense *see* tense.

principal clause *see* main clause.

progressive present *see* tense.

pronoun

A word that takes the place of a NOUN or a NOUN PHRASE. *See* PERSONAL PRONOUNS, HE, HER, HIM, and HIS, RECIPROCAL PRONOUNS, REFLEXIVE PRONOUNS, DEMONSTRATIVE PRONOUNS, RELATIVE PRONOUNS, DISTRIBUTIVE PRONOUNS, INDEFINITE PRONOUNS, and INTERROGATIVE PRONOUNS.

proper noun

A noun that refers to a particular individual or a specific thing—the name of someone or something, as in California, Rocky Mountains, Martin Luther King, Hudson River, Philadelphia, and Atlantic Ocean. *See* CAPITAL LETTERS.

punctuation

The use of punctuation marks within a written text to enhance its meaning or fluency or to indicate aspects of pronunciation.

punctuation mark

One of the standardized symbols used in punctuation, such as the PERIOD, COLON, SEMICOLON, COMMA, QUESTION MARK, etc.

Q

question mark

The punctuation mark (?) that is placed at the end of a question or interrogative sentence, as in "Who is he?", "Where are they?", "Why have they gone?", "Whereabouts are they?", "When are you going?", and "What did he say?" The question mark is sometimes known as the **interrogation point**.

question tag

A phrase that is interrogative in form but is not really asking a question. It is added to a statement to seek agreement, etc. Examples include "That was a lovely meal, wasn't it?", "You will be able to go, won't you?", "He's not going to move house, is he?" and "She doesn't drive, does she?" Sentences containing question tags have question marks at the end.

quotation marks *or* quotes

Punctuation marks that are used in DIRECT SPEECH. Quotation marks are also used to enclose titles of newspapers, books, plays, films, musical works, and works of art, as in "Washington Post," "Animal Farm," "Othello," "My Fair Lady," and "A Portrait of the Artist as a Young Man." Quotation marks may consist of a set of single inverted commas (' ') or a set of double inverted commas (" "). If a title, etc., is to be enclosed in quotation marks and the title is part of a piece of writing already in quotation marks for some other reason, such as being part of direct speech, then the quotation marks around the title should be in the type of quotation marks opposite to the other ones. Thus, if the piece of writing is in single quotation marks, then the title should be in double quotation marks, as in 'Have you read "Wuthering Heights"?' If the piece of writing is in double quotation marks, the title should be in single quotation marks, as in "Did you go to see 'Chicago'?"

R

re-

A common prefix meaning "again" in verbs. In most cases it is not followed by a hyphen, as in "to retrace one's footsteps," "a retrial ordered by the judge," and "to reconsider his decision." However, it should be followed by a hyphen if its absence is likely to lead to confusion with another word, as in "re-cover a chair"/"recover from an illness," "re-count the votes"/"recount a tale of woe," "the re-creation of a 17th-century village for a movie set"/"play tennis for recreation," and "re-form the group"/"reform the prison system." In cases where the second element of a word begins with *e*, re- is traditionally followed by a hyphen, as in "re-educate," "re-entry" and "re-echo," but in modern usage the hyphen is frequently omitted.

reciprocal pronoun

A pronoun used to convey the idea of reciprocity or a two-way relationship. The reciprocal pronouns are "each other" and "one another." Examples include "They don't love each other anymore," "They seem to hate each other," "We must try to help each other," "The children were calling one another names," "The two families were always criticizing one another," and "The members of the family blame one another for their mother's death."

reciprocal verb

A verb such as "consult," "embrace," "marry," "meet," etc., that expresses a mutual relationship, as in "They met at the conference," "She married him in June."

reduplication

The process by which words are created by repetition or by semi-repetition. These include "dilly-dally," "shilly-shally," "flimflam," "heebie-jeebies," "hocus-pocus," "hugger-mugger," "knick-knack," and "mish-mash."

reflexive pronoun

A pronoun that ends in "-self" or "-selves" and refers back to a noun or pronoun that has occurred earlier in the same sentence. The reflexive pronouns include "myself," "ourselves"; "yourself," "yourselves"; "himself," "herself," "itself," "themselves." Examples include "The children washed themselves," "He cut himself shaving," "Have you hurt yourself?", and "She broke herself of the habit."

Reflexive pronouns are sometimes used for emphasis, as in "The town itself was not very interesting" and "The principal himself punished the boys." They can also be used to indicate that something has been done by somebody by his/her own efforts without any help, as in "He built the house himself," "We converted the attic ourselves." They can also indicate that someone or something is alone, as in "She lives by herself" and "The house stands by itself."

reflexive verb

A verb that has as its direct object a REFLEXIVE PRONOUN, e.g. "They pride themselves on their skill as a team."

regular sentence *see* major sentence.

regular verb *see* irregular verb.

relative clause

A SUBORDINATE CLAUSE that has the function of an adjective. It is introduced by a RELATIVE PRONOUN.

relative pronoun

A pronoun that introduces a RELATIVE CLAUSE. The relative pronouns are "who," "whom," "whose," "which," and "that." Examples of relative clauses introduced by relative pronouns include "There is the man who stole the money," "She is the person to whom I gave the money," "This is the man whose wife won the prize," "They criticized the work which he had done," and "That's the house that I would like to buy." Relative pronouns refer back to a NOUN or NOUN PHRASE in the MAIN CLAUSE. These nouns and noun phrases are known as ANTECEDENTS. The antecedents in the example sentences are respectively "man," "person," "man," "work" and "house."

Sometimes the relative clause divides the parts of the main clause, as in "The woman whose daughter is ill is very upset," "The people whom we met on vacation were French" and "The house that we liked best was too expensive."

reported speech *see* **indirect speech**.

retro-

A prefix derived from Latin meaning "back, backward," as in retro-grade, retrospect, retrorocket.

retronym

A word or phrase that has had to be renamed slightly in the light of another invention, etc. For example, an ordinary guitar became an "acoustic guitar" because of the existence of the "electric guitar." Leather has sometimes become "real leather" because of the exist-ence of "imitation leather."

rhetorical question

A question that is asked to achieve some kind of effect and requires no answer. Examples include "What is this country com-ing to?", "Did you ever see the like?", "Why do these things happen to me?", "Where did our youth go?", "Death, where is thy sting?", and "Where does time go?" *See also* INTERROGATIVE SENTENCE.

Roman type

The normal upright type used in printing, not BOLD or ITALIC type.

root *see* **base**.

S

second person

The term used for the person or thing to whom one is talking. The term is applied to PERSONAL PRONOUNS. The second person singular whether acting as the subject or the object of a sentence is "you," as in "I told you so," "We informed you of our decision," and "You might have asked us sooner." The second person personal pronoun does not alter its form in the plural in English, unlike in some languages. The possessive form of the second person pronoun is "yours" whether singular or plural, as in "These books are not yours" and "This pen must be yours."

semicolon

A rather formal form of punctuation. It is mainly used between clauses that are not joined by any form of conjunction, as in "We had a wonderful vacation; sadly they did not," "She was my sister; she was also my best friend," and "He was a marvelous friend; he is much missed." A DASH is sometimes used instead of a semicolon but this is more informal.

The semicolon is also used to form subsets in a long list or series of names so that the said list seems less complex, as in "The young man who wants to be a journalist has applied everywhere. He has applied to *The Times* in London; *The Globe and Mail* in Toronto; *The Age* in Melbourne; *The Tribune* in Chicago."

The semicolon is also sometimes used before "however," "nevertheless," "hence," etc., as in "We have extra seats for the concert; however you must not feel obliged to come."

sentence

This is at the head of the hierarchy of grammar. All the other elements, such as words, phrases, and clauses, go to make up sentences. It is difficult to define a sentence. In terms of recognizing a sentence visually it can be described as beginning with a capital letter and ending with a period, or with an equivalent to the period, such as an exclamation point. It is a unit of grammar that can stand alone and make sense and obeys certain grammatical rules, such as usually having a SUBJECT and a PREDICATE, as in "The girl banged the door," where "the girl" is the subject and "the door" is the predicate. *See* MAJOR SENTENCE, SIMPLE SENTENCE, COMPLEX SENTENCE.

set phrase *see* **fixed phrase**.

sexism
The domination of male values, which was formerly widespread in the English language whether this was intentional or not. Efforts are now being made to rectify this situation, although some of the suggestions made are rather extreme. Sensible progress has, however, been made. *See* HE; EACH; -MAN; -PERSON.

simile
A figure of speech in which something is compared with another and said to be like it. This is in contradistinction to METAPHOR, where one thing is said actually to be another. Examples of similes include "She is like an angel," "Her hair is like silk," "The old man's skin is like leather," "He swims like a fish."

simple sentence
A SENTENCE that cannot be broken down into other clauses. It generally contains a FINITE VERB. Simple sentences include "The man stole the car," "She nudged him," and "He kicked the ball." *See* COMPLEX SENTENCE, COMPOUND SENTENCE.

singular noun
A noun that refers to "one" rather than "more than one," which is the PLURAL form. *See also* IRREGULAR PLURAL.

spelling *see* **Appendix 1**.

split infinitive
An infinitive that has had another word in the form of an adverb placed between itself and "to," as in "to rudely push" and "to

quietly leave." This was once considered a great grammatical sin but the split infinitive is becoming acceptable in modern usage. In any case, it sometimes makes for a clumsy sentence if one slavishly adheres to the correct form.

spoonerism

The accidental or deliberate transposition of the initial letters of two or more words, as in "the queer old dean" instead of "the dear old queen," "a blushing crow" instead of a "crushing blow," and "a well-boiled icicle" instead of a "well-oiled bicycle." Spoonerisms are called after the Reverend William Archibald Spooner (1844–1930) of Oxford University.

stative present *see* **habitual** *and* **tense**.

stem *see* **base**.

strong verb

The more common term for IRREGULAR VERB.

structure word *see* **function word**.

subject

That which is spoken of in a sentence or clause and is usually either a NOUN, as in "Birds fly" ("birds" is the noun as subject); a NOUN PHRASE, as in "The people in the town dislike him" ("the people in the town" is the subject); a PRONOUN, as in "She hit the child" ("she" is the pronoun as subject); a PROPER NOUN, as in "Paris is the capital of France" ("Paris" is the subject). *See* DUMMY SUBJECT.

subjunctive *see* **mood**.

subordinate clause

A clause that is dependent on another clause, namely the MAIN CLAUSE. Unlike the main clause, it cannot stand alone and make sense. Subordinate clauses are introduced by CONJUNCTIONS. Examples of conjunctions that introduce subordinate clauses include "after," "before," "when," "if," "because," and "since." *See* ADVERBIAL CLAUSE; NOUN CLAUSE.

subordinating conjunction *see* **conjunction**.

suffix

An AFFIX that goes at the end of a word. The affix "-ness" is a suffix in "softness" and "preparedness."

superlative form

The form of an adjective or adverb that expresses the highest or utmost degree of the quality or manner of the word. The superlative forms follow the same rules as comparative forms except that they end in *-est* instead of *-er* and the longer ones use "most" instead of "more." *See also* COMPARISON OF ADJECTIVES.

syllepsis *see* **zeugma**.

synecdoche

A figure of speech in which the part is put for the whole. For example, in "The power of the scepter is fading," "scepter" is used for "monarch"; in "The country has a fleet of a hundred sail," "sail" is used for "ship"; in "The actor had a very successful career on the boards," "boards" is used for "stage."

T

tautology

Unnecessary repetition, as in "new innovations," "a see-through transparent material" and "one after the other in succession."

techno-

A prefix derived from Greek meaning "craft, skill," as in technical, technology, technique.

tele-

A prefix derived from Greek meaning "distance," as in telephone, telescope, television.

tense

The form of a verb that is used to show the time at which the action of the verb takes place. One of the tenses in English is the **present tense**. It is used to indicate an action now going on or a state now existing. A distinction can be made between the **habitual present**, which marks habitual or repeated actions or recurring events, and the **stative present**, which indicates something that is true at all times. Examples of habitual present include "He works long hours" and "She walks to work." Examples of the stative tense include "The world is round" and "Everyone must die eventually."

The **progressive present** or **continuous present** is formed with the verb "to be" and the present participle, as in, "He is walking to the next village," "She was driving along the road when she saw him," and "They were worrying about the state of the economy."

The **past tense** refers to an action or state that has taken place before the present time. In the case of regular verbs it is formed by adding *-ed* to the base form of the verb, as in "fear/feared," "look/looked," and "turn/turned." *See also* IRREGULAR VERBS.

The **future tense** refers to an action or state that will take place at some time in the future. It is formed with "will" and "shall." Traditionally "will" was used with the second and third person pronouns ("you," "he/she/it," "they") and "shall" with the first person ("I" and "we"), as in "You will be bored," "He will soon be home," "They will leave tomorrow," "I shall buy some bread," and "We shall go by train." Also traditionally, "shall" was used with the second and third persons to indicate emphasis, insistence, determination, refusal, etc., as in "You shall go to the ball" and "He shall not be admitted." "Will" was used with the first person in the same way, as in "I will get even with him."

In modern usage "will" is generally used for the first person as well as for second and third, as in "I will see you tomorrow" and "We will be there soon" and "shall" is used for emphasis, insistence, etc., for first, second, and third persons.

The future tense can also be formed with the use of "be about to" or "be going to," as in "We were about to leave" and "They were going to look for a house."

Other tenses include the **perfect tense**, which is formed using the verb "to have" and the past participle. In the case of regular verbs the past participle is formed by adding -*ed* to the base form of the verb. *See also* IRREGULAR VERBS. Examples of the perfect tense include "He has played his last game," "We have traveled all day," and "They have thought a lot about it."

The **past perfect tense** or **pluperfect tense** is formed using the verb "to have" and the past participle, as in "She had no idea that he was dead" and "They had felt unhappy about the situation."

The **future perfect** is formed using the verb "to have" and the past participle, as in "He will have arrived by now."

the

The definite article, which usually refers back to something already identified or to something specific, as in "Where is the key?", "What have you done with the book that I gave you?", and "We have found the book that had we lost." It is also used to denote someone or something as being the only one, as in "the House of Lords," "the King of Spain," and "the President of the USA" and to indicate a class or group, as in "the aristocracy," "the cat family," and "the teaching profession." The is sometimes pronounced "thee" when it is used to identify someone or something unique or important, as in "Is that the John Frame over there?" and "She is the fashion designer of the moment."

they *see* **he**.

third person

A third party, not the speaker or the person or thing being spoken to. Note that "person" in this context can refer to things as well as people. "Person" in this sense applies to personal pronouns. The third person singular forms are "he," "she," and "it" when the subject of a sentence or clause, as in "She will win" and "It will be fine." The third person singular forms are "him," "her," "it" when the object, as in "His behavior hurt her" and "She meant it." The third person plural is "they" when the subject, as in "They have left" and "They were angry," and "them" when the object, as in "His words made them angry" and "We accompanied them."

The possessive forms of the singular are "his," "hers," and "its," as in "He played his guitar" and "The dog hurt its leg," and the possessive form of the plural is theirs, as in "That car is theirs" and "They say that the book is theirs." *See* HE.

to-infinitive

The INFINITIVE form of the verb when it is accompanied by "to" rather than when it is the bare infinitive without "to." Examples of the to-infinitive include "We were told to go," "I didn't want to stay," and "To get there on time we'll have to leave now."

transitive verb

A verb that takes a DIRECT OBJECT. In the sentence "The boy broke the window," "window" is a direct object and so "broke" (past tense of break) is a transitive verb. In the sentence "She eats fruit," "fruit" is a direct object and so "eat" is a transitive verb. In the sentence "They kill enemy soldiers," "enemy soldiers" is a direct object and so "kill" is a transitive verb. *See* INTRANSITIVE VERB.

U

ultra-
A prefix derived from Latin meaning "beyond," as in ultraviolet, ultramodern.

umlaut
The DIACRITIC, which indicates a change of vowel sound in German, as in *Mädchen*.

un-
A prefix with two meanings. It can mean either "not," as in unclean, untrue, unwise. It can also mean "back, reversal," as in undo, unfasten, unlatch, untie.

uncountable noun *the same as* **mass noun**.

uni-
A prefix derived from Latin meaning "one," as in unicycle, unilateral, unity.

V

verb

The part of speech often known as a "doing" word. Although this is rather restrictive, since it tends to preclude AUXILIARY VERBS, MODAL VERBS, etc., the verb is the word in a sentence that is most concerned with the action and is usually essential to the structure of the sentence. Verbs "INFLECT" and indicate TENSE, voice, mood, number, and person. Most of the information on verbs has been placed under related entries. *See* ACTIVE VOICE, AUXILIARY VERB, FINITE VERB, -ING FORMS, INTRANSITIVE VERB, IRREGULAR VERBS, LINKING VERB, MODAL VERB, MOOD, NON-FINITE VERB, PASSIVE VOICE, and TRANSITIVE VERB.

verbal noun *see* gerund *and* -ing form.

verb phrase

A group of verb forms that have the same function as a single verb. Examples include "have been raining," "must have been lying," "should not have been doing," and "has been seen doing."

virgule

A rare word for an oblique. *See* OBLIQUE.

vocative case

A case that is relevant mainly to languages such as Latin, which are based on cases and inflections. In English the vocative is expressed by addressing someone, as in "John, could I see you for a minute?" or by some form of greeting, endearment, or exclamation.

voice

One of the categories that describe verbs. It involves two ways of looking at the action of verbs. It is divided into ACTIVE VOICE and PASSIVE VOICE.

W

-ways

A suffix that to some extent acts as an alternative to -WISE in its first two meanings, as in lengthways.

weak verb

A less common term for a regular verb, in which inflection is effected by adding a letter or syllable (dawn, dawned) rather than a change of vowel (rise, rose). *See* IRREGULAR VERB.

who *and* whom

Who is the SUBJECT of a verb or clause, as in "Who told you?" and "the girls who took part in the play." **Whom** is the OBJECT of a verb or preposition, as in "Whom did he tell?" and "the people from whom he stole."

whose *and* who's

These are liable to be confused because they sound the same. However they are not at all the same. **Who's** is a contraction of "who is" and is used in speech and informal written contexts, as in "Who's going to the movies?" and "Who's afraid of spiders?" **Whose** is a possessive pronoun or possessive adjective, as in "That's the woman whose house was burgled" and "Whose hat is this?"

-wise

A suffix with several meanings. It can mean "indicating manner or way," as in clockwise. It can also mean "in the position or direction of," as in lengthwise and breadthwise. It can also mean "with reference to," as in careerwise. It can also mean "clever, sensible," as in streetwise.

Z

zero plural

A plural form that has the same form as the singular. Examples include "cod," "deer," "grouse" (game-bird), and "sheep." Some nouns have ordinary plurals and zero plurals as alternatives, as "fish/fishes." Nouns of measurement often have zero plurals, as in "She is five foot three" and "Six dozen eggs."

zeugma *or* syllepsis

A figure of speech that uses a single word to apply to two words that are not appropriate to each other, as in "We collected our coats and our baby," "She left the building and her job," and "She left in a taxi and a fit of hysterics." Zeugma is similar to BATHOS.

APPENDIX 1

All of us have problem words that cause spelling difficulties but there are some words that are generally misspelt. These include:

A
abbreviation
abscess
absence
abysmal
accelerator
accessible
accessories
accommodate
accompaniment
accumulate
accurate
accustomed
achieve
aching
acknowledge
acknowledg-
ment
acquaint
acquaintance
acquiesce
acquiescence
acquire
acquit
acquittal
acreage
across
actual
additional
address
adequate
adieu
adjacent
admissible
admittance

adolescence
adolescent
advantageous
advertisement
advice
advise
aerate
acrial
affect
affiliation
afforestation
aggravate
aggravation
aggregate
aggression
aggressive
aghast
agnosticism
agoraphobia
agreeable
agreed
agreed
aisle
alcohol
alfresco
alibis
align
alignment
allege
allergic
alleys
alligator
allocate
allotment
allotted
almond

alms
alphabetically
already
although
aluminum
ambiguous
amethyst
ammunition
anachronism
analysis
analyze
anarchist
ancestor
ancestry
anemone
anesthetic
angrily
anguish
annihilate
annihilation
anniversary
announcement
annulled
annulment
anonymous
answered
Antarctic
antibiotic
antithesis
anxiety
apartheid
apologize
appalling
apparently
appearance

appendicitis
appreciate
approval
aquarium
aquiline
arbiter
arbitrary
arbitration
archeology
architectural
Arctic
arguably
arrangement
arrival
artichoke
ascend
ascent
asphalt
asphyxiate
asphyxiation
assassin
assassinate
assessment
assistance
associate
asthma
asthmatic
astrakhan
atheist
atrocious
attach
attendant
attitude
attorney
auburn

auctioneer
audible
aural
automatic
awful
awkward

B
bachelor
bagatelle
baggage
bailiff
ballast
ballerina
banana
banister
bankruptcy
banquet
barbecue
barometer
basically
basis
bassoon
battalion
bazaar
beautiful
befriend
beguile
behavior
beleaguer
belief
believe
belligerent
benefited
bequeath
berserk
besiege
bettered
beveled
bewitch
bias
bicycle
biennial

bigamous
bigoted
bilingual
biscuit
bivouacked
bizarre
blancmange
blasphemous
blasphemy
bleary
blitz
bodily
bonfire
bootee
borough
bouquet
bourgeois
boutique
bracketed
braille
brassiere
breadth
Breathalyzer
brief
broccoli
brochure
bronchitis
bruise
brusque
buccaneer
Buddhist
budding
budgerigar
budgeted
buffeted
bulletin
bumptious
bungalow
buoyancy
buoyant
bureau
bureaucracy
business
buttoned

C
cabbage
cafeteria
caffeine
camouflage
campaign
campaigner
cancellation
cancerous
candor
cannabis
cannibal
canvassing
capability
capillary
capitalist
caravan
carbohydrate
carburetor
career
caress
caries
carriage
cartoonist
cashier
cassette
castanets
casualty
catalog
catarrh
catechism
catering
cauliflower
cautious
ceiling
cellophane
cemetery
centenary
centiliter
centimeter
certainty
champagne
championed
chancellor

changeable
channeled
characteristic
chasm
chauffeur
cheetah
cherish
chief
chilblain
chintz
chiropody
chiseled
choreographer
choreography
chronically
chrysanthemum
cigarette
cinnamon
circuitous
cistern
civilian
claustrophobia
clientele
clique
coalesce
cocoa
coconut
coffee
cognac
coincidence
colander
collaborate
collapsible
colleague
colonel
colossal
comically
commandeer
commemorate
commencement
commentator
commercial
commiserate
commission

commitment
committal
committed
committee
communicate
commuter
companion
comparative
comparison
compatibility
compelled
competitive
computer
conceal
concealment
conceit
conceive
concession
concurrent
concussion
condemned
condescend
confectionery
conference
confetti
congeal
congratulations
conjunctivitis
conned
connoisseur
conscience
conscientious
conscious
consequently
consignment
consolation
conspicuous
constitute
consumer
contemptible
continent
continuous
contraception
contradictory

controlled
controller
controversial
convalesce
convenient
convertible
conveyed
convolvulus
coolly
cooperate
cooperative
coordinate
copying
coquette
corduroy
corespondent
coronary
correspondence
correspondent
corridor
corroborate
corrugated
cosmopolitan
cosseted
councilor
counseling
counterfeit
courageous
courteous
crèche
credible
credited
crematorium
creosote
crescent
crisis
criterion
crocheted
crocodile
croupier
crucial
crucifixion
cruelly
cruise

cryptic
cubicle
cupful
curable
curiosity
curious
currency
curriculum vitae
customary
cynic
cynicism
cynosure

D
dachshund
daffodil
dahlia
dais
damage
dandruff
darkened
debatable
debauched
debility
deceased
deceit
deceive
deciduous
decipher
decoyed
decrease
decreed
defamatory
defeat
defendant
defense
defied
definite
definitely
dehydrate
deign
deliberate
delicatessen
delicious

delinquent
delirious
demeanor
demonstrate
denouement
denunciation
dependence
depth
derailment
dermatitis
derogatory
descend
descendant
desiccate
desperate
detach
detachable
detergent
deterred
deterrent
deuce
develop
developed
development
diabetes
diagnosis
dialog
diametrically
diaphragm
diarrhea
difference
different
dilapidated
dilemma
dilettante
diminish
diminution
dinosaur
diphtheria
diphthong
disadvantageous
disagreeable
disagreed
disagreement

disappearance
disappeared
disappoint
disapproval
disastrous
disbelief
disbelieve
discipline
discotheque
discouraging
discourteous
discrepancy
discrimination
discussion
disease
disguise
disheveled
dishonorable
disillusion
disinfectant
disinherited
dismissal
disobeyed
disparage
dispelled
disposal
dispossess
dissatisfaction
dissatisfy
dissect
disseminate
dissent
dissimilar
dissipated
dissipation
dissociate
dissolute
dissuade
distilled
distillery
distinguish
distraught
disuse
divisible

documentary
doggerel
domineering
donate
doubt
drafty
dragooned
drastically
drooled
drooped
drunkenness
dubious
dumbfounded
dungarees
duress
dutiful
dynamite
dysentery
dyspepsia

E
eccentric
ecclesiastic
ecologically
economically
ecstasy
eczema
effective
effervescence
efficacious
efficient
effrontery
eightieth
elaborate
electrician
elevator
eligible
emancipate
embarrass
embarrassment
emergence
emergent
emolument
emotional

emphasize
employee
emptied
enable
encourage
encyclopedia
endeavor
endurance
energetically
enervate
engineer
enough
ensuing
entailed
enthusiasm
enumerate
epilepsy
equaled
equalize
equipped
erroneous
erudite
escalator
escapism
espionage
essence
essential
esthetic
estranged
etiquette
euthanasia
eventually
evidently
exaggerate
exaggeration
exalt
exasperate
exceed
exceedingly
excellent
excessive
exchequer
excommunicate
exercise

exhaust
exhibit
exhilarate
exorcise
explanation
exquisite
extinguish
extraneous
extravagant

F
fabulous
facetious
Fahrenheit
fallacious
fanatic
farcical
fascinate
fatigue
fatuous
February
feces
feeler
feign
ferocious
festooned
feud
feudal
fevered
fiasco
fiber
fictitious
fiend
fierce
fiery
filial
finesse
flabbergasted
flaccid
flammable
flannelette
fluent
fluoridate
fluoride

fluoridize
foliage
forcible
foreigner
forfeit
forthwith
fortieth
fortuitous
fortunately
frailty
frankincense
fraudulent
freedom
freight
frequency
friend
frolicked
fuchsia
fugitive
fulfill
fulfillment
fullness
fully
fulsome
furious
furniture
furthered

G
gaiety
galloped
garrison
garroted
gases
gateau
gauge
gazetteer
geisha
generator
genuine
gerbil
gesticulate
ghastly
ghetto

gigantic
gingham
giraffe
glamor
glamorous
glimpse
global
gluttonous
glycerin
gnarled
gnash
goiter
gossiped
government
graffiti
grammar
grandeur
gratefully
gratitude
gratuitous
greetings
gregarious
grief
grieve
groveled
gruesome
guarantee
guarantor
guard
guardian
guest
guillotine
guinea
guise
guitar
gymkhana
Gypsy

H
halcyon
hallucination
hammered
handfuls
handicapped

handkerchief
happened
harangue
harass
harlequin
haughty
hazard
hearse
height
heightened
heinous
heir
hemoglobin
hemorrhage
herbaceous
hereditary
heroism
hesitate
hiccup
hideous
hierarchy
hieroglyphics
hijack
hilarious
hindrance
hippopotamus
holiday
holocaust
homonym
honor
honorary
hooligan
horoscope
horrible
horticulture
hullabaloo
humor
humorous
hurricane
hurried
hygiene
hyphen
hypnosis
hypochondria

hypocrisy
hypotenuse
hypothesis
hypothetical
hysterical

I
icicle
ideological
idiosyncrasy
ignorance
illegible
illegitimate
illiberal
illiterate
imaginative
imitation
immaculate
immediate
immemorial
immoral
immovable
impasse
impeccable
imperative
imperceptible
imperious
impetuous
implacable
impresario
imprisoned
imprisonment
inaccessible
inadmissible
inappropriate
inaugural
incandescent
incessant
incipient
incognito
incommunicado
inconceivable
incongruous
incontrovertible

incorrigible
incredulous
incriminate
incubator
incurred
indefatigable
indefinable
indefinite
independence
independent
indescribable
indict
indictment
indigenous
indigestible
indomitable
indubitable
ineligible
inescapable
inexcusable
inexhaustible
infallible
infatuated
inferred
infinitive
inflamed
inflammable
inflationary
ingratiate
ingredient
inhabitant
inheritance
inhibition
iniquitous
initiate
initiative
innate
innocuous
innumerable
innumerate
inoculate
insecticide
inseparable
insincere

insistence
installment
instantaneous
intercept
interference
interior
intermediate
intermittent
interpret
interpretation
interrogate
interrupt
interview
intrigue
intrinsically
intuition
intuitive
invariably
inveigle
inveterate
involuntary
involvement
irascible
irrelevant
irreparable
irreplaceable
irresistible
irresponsible
irrevocable
irritable
italicize
itinerant
itinerary

J
jackal
Jacuzzi
jeopardize
jettisoned
jewelry
jodhpurs
juggernaut
jugular

K
kaleidoscopic
karate
keenness
khaki
kidnapped
kilometer
kiosk
kitchenette
kleptomania
knickknack
knowledgeable
kowtow

L
labeled
laboratory
labyrinth
lackadaisical
laddered
lager
language
languor
languorous
laryngitis
larynx
lassitude
latitude
laundered
launderette
layette
league
leanness
ledger
legendary
legible
legitimate
length
lengthened
leukemia
leveled
liaise
liaison
lieu

lieutenant
lilac
limousine
lineage
linen
lingerie
linguist
liqueur
liquor
liter
literature
livelihood
loneliness
loosened
loquacious
lorgnette
lucrative
lucre
lugubrious
luminous
luscious
luster
lustrous
luxurious
lyric

M
macabre
maelstrom
magician
magnanimous
mahogany
maintenance
malaise
malaria
malignant
manageable
management
maneuver
mannequin
mantelpiece
manually
margarine
marijuana

marquee
martyr
marvelous
marzipan
masochist
massacre
matinee
mayonnaise
meager
measurement
medallion
medieval
mediocre
melancholy
meningitis
meringue
messenger
meteorological
metropolitan
microphone
midday
migraine
milage
milieu
millionaire
mimicked
mimicry
miniature
miraculous
mirrored
miscellaneous
mischief
mischievous
misogynist
misshapen
misspell
misspent
modeled
modeling
morgue
mortgage
mosquito
mountaineer
multitudinous

muscle
museum
mustache
mysterious
mythical

N
naive
narrative
naughty
nausea
nautical
necessary
necessity
negligence
negligible
negotiate
neighborhood
neither
neurotic
neutral
niche
niece
ninetieth
ninth
nocturnal
nonentity
notably
noticeably
notoriety
nuance
numbered
numerate
numerous
nutrient
nutritious

O
obedient
obese
obituary
oblige

oblique
oblivious
obnoxious
obscene
obscenity
obsessive
obstetrician
occasion
occupancy
occupier
occupying
occurred
occurrence
octogenarian
odor
odorous
offense
offered
official
officious
ominous
omission
omitted
oneself
opaque
ophthalmic
opinion
opponent
opportunity
opposite
orchestra
ordinary
original
orthodox
orthopedic
oscillate
ostracize
outlying
outrageous
overdraft
overrate
overreach
overwrought
oxygen

P
pacifist
pageant
pajamas
pamphlet
panacea
panegyric
panicked
papered
parachute
paraffin
paragraph
paralysis
paralyze
paraphernalia
parceled
parliament
paroxysm
parquet
partially
participant
particle
partner
passenger
passers-by
pastime
patterned
pavilion
peaceable
peculiar
pejorative
penciled
penicillin
peppered
perceive
perennial
perilous
permissible
permitted
pernicious
perpetrate
persistence
personnel
persuasion

perusal
pessimism
pessimistically
pesticide
phantom
pharmacy
pharyngitis
pharynx
phenomenon
phial
phlegm
physician
picketed
picnic
picnicked
picturesque
pioneered
pious
piteous
pitiful
plaintiff
plausible
pleurisy
pneumonia
poignant
politician
pollution
polyethylene
porridge
portrait
portray
positive
possession
possibility
posthumous
potatoes
precede
precedent
precinct
precipice
precocious
preference
preferred
prejudice

preliminary
prepossessing
prerequisite
prerogative
prescription
presence
preservative
prestige
prestigious
pretentious
prevalent
priest
primitive
procedure
proceed
procession
professional
profiteering
prohibit
promiscuous
pronunciation
propeller
proposal
proprietor
prosecute
protagonist
protein
provocation
prowess
psalm
psyche
psychiatric
psychic
publicly
pursuit
putative

Q
quarrelsome
questionnaire
quiche
quintet

R
rabies
radioed
radios
railing
rancor
ransack
rapturous
reassurance
rebelled
rebellious
recalcitrant
receipt
receive
recommend
reconnaissance
reconnoiter
recruitment
recurrence
redundant
referee
reference
referred
regatta
regrettable
regretted
rehabilitation
reign
relevant
relief
relieve
reminisce
reminiscence
remuneration
rendezvous
repertoire
repetitive
reprieve
reprisal
requisite
rescind
resemblance
reservoir
resistance

resourceful
responsibility
restaurant
restaurateur
resurrection
resuscitate
retrieve
reunion
reveille
revelry
revenue
reversible
rhapsody
rheumatism
rhododendron
rhomboid
rhubarb
rhyme
rhythm
ricochet
righteous
rigor
rigorous
risotto
riveted
rogue
roughage
roulette
royalty
rucksack
ruinous
rummage
rumor

S
sabotage
sacrilege
saddened
salmon
salvage
sanctuary
sandwich
sanitary

sapphire	slanderous	subtle	teenager
satellite	slaughter	succeed	televise
scaffolding	sleigh	successful	temperature
scandalous	sleight of hand	successor	tenuous
scenic	sluice	succinct	terrifically
scepter	smattering	succulent	terrifying
schedule	smithereens	succumb	territory
scheme	sniveled	suddenness	terrorist
schizophrenic	soccer	suede	therapeutic
schooner	solemn	sufficient	therefore
sciatica	solicit	suffocate	thief
science	soliloquy	suicide	thinness
scissors	soloist	sullenness	thirtieth
scruple	somber	summoned	thorough
scrupulous	somersault	supercilious	thoroughfare
scurrilous	sophisticated	superfluous	threshold
scythe	sovereign	supersede	thrombosis
secretarial	spaghetti	supervise	throughout
secretary	specter	supervisor	thwart
sedative	spherical	supplementary	thyme
sedentary	sphinx	surgeon	tightened
sensitive	sponsor	surveillance	titivate
separate	spontaneity	surveyor	tobacconist
sergeant	spontaneous	susceptible	toboggan
serrated	squabble	suspicious	toffee
serviceable	squandered	sweetener	tomatoes
serviette	squawk	sycamore	tomorrow
settee	staccato	symmetry	tonsillitis
shampooed	staggered	sympathize	topsy-turvy
shattered	stammered	symphony	tornadoes
sheik	statistics	synagogue	torpedoes
sheriff	statutory	syndicate	torpor
shield	stealth	synonym	tortoiseshell
shoveled	stereophonic	syringe	tortuous
shuddered	stirrup		totaled
siege	storage		tourniquet
significant	straitjacket	T	toweling
silhouette	strait-laced		trafficked
simply	strategic	tableau	tragedy
simultaneous	strength	taciturn	traitorous
sincerely	strenuous	taffeta	tranquilizer
sixtieth	stupor	tangerine	tranquilly
skeleton	suave	tangible	transcend
skillful	subpoena	tattoo	transferable
		technique	

transferred
transparent
traveled
traveler
tremor
troublesome
trousseau
truism
trustee
tsetse
tuberculosis
tumor
tunneled
tureen
turquoise
twelfth
typhoon
tyranny

U
unanimous
unconscious
undoubted
unduly
unequaled

unique
unnecessary
unremitting
unrequited
unrivaled
upheaval
uproarious

V
vaccinate
vacuum
vague
vanilla
variegate
vehement
vendetta
veneer
ventilator
veranda
vermilion
veterinarian
vetoes
vice versa
vicissitude
vigor

vigorous
viscount
visibility
vivacious
vociferous
voluminous
volunteered
vulnerable

W
walkie-talkie
walloped
warrior
wastage
watered
weakened
wearisome
Wednesday
weight
weird
whereabouts
wherewithal
widened
width
wield

wintry
witticism
wizened
woebegone
wooden
woolen
worsened
worship
worshiped
wrapper
wrath
wreak
writhe

X
xylophone

Y
yield
yogurt

Z
zealous
zigzagged
zucchini

APPENDIX 2

Some words with totally different meanings have similar spellings and therefore can be easily confused. Some examples are:

aboard	abroad	artist	artiste
accept	except	ascent	assent
access	excess	ascetic	esthetic
acme	acne	assay	essay
ad	add	assent	ascent
adapt	adopt	astrology	astronomy
addition	edition	ate	eaten
adverse	averse	aural	oral
advice	advise	averse	adverse
aesthetic	ascetic	awl	all
affect	effect	axes	axis
affluent	effluent	bad	bade
ail	ale	bade	bid
air	heir	bail	bale
all	awl		bale out
allay	alley	baited	bated
allegory	allergy	ball	bawl
alley	allay	ballet	ballot
allitcrate	illiterate	banns	bans
allude	elude	bare	bear
allusion	delusion	harn	barren
	illusion	base	bass
altar	alter	bated	baited
alteration	altercation	bath	bathe
alternately	alternatively	baton	batten
amateur	amateurish	bawl	ball
amend	emend	bazaar	bizarre
amiable	amicable	beach	beech
among	between	bean	been
amoral	immoral		being
	immortal	beat	beet
angel	angle	beau	bow
annals	annuals	became	become
annuals	annals	beech	beach
antiquated	antique	been	bean
arc	ark		being
arisen	arose	beer	bier

175

beet	beat	bouquet	bookie
befallen	befell	bow	beau
began	begun	bow	bough
being	bean	boy	buoy
	been	brae	bray
belief	believe	brake	break
bell	belle	brassiere	brazier
bellow	below	bray	brae
beret	berry	brazier	brassiere
	bury	breach	breech
berth	birth	bread	bred
beside	besides	break	brake
between	among	breath	breathe
bid	bade	bred	bread
bier	beer	breech	breach
bight	bite	bridal	bridle
birth	berth	broach	brooch
bit	bitten	broke	broken
bite	bight	brooch	broach
bizarre	bazaar	buffet	buffet
blew	blown	[buffit]	[boofay]
blew	blue	buoy	boy
bloc	block	burgh	borough
blond	blonde	bury	beret
blow	blown		berry
	blew	but	butt
blue	blew	buy	by
boar	boor		bye
	bore	cache	cash
board	bored	caddie	caddy
boast	boost	calf	calve
bonny	bony	callous	callus
bookie	bouquet	calve	calf
boor	boar	came	come
	bore	canned	could
boost	boast	cannon	canon
bootee	booty	can't	cant
bore	boar	canvas	canvass
	boor	carat	carrot
bore	born	cartilage	cartridge
	borne	carton	cartoon
borough	burgh	cartridge	cartilage
bough	bow	cash	cache
bound	bounded	cast	caste

cavalier	cavalry	co-respondent	correspondent
ceiling	sealing	cornet	coronet
cell	sell	coronet	cornet
cellular	cellulose	corps	corpse
censor	censure	corral	coral
cent	scent	correspondent	co-respondent
	sent	cost	costed
centenarian	centenary	could	canned
cereal	serial	council	counsel
chafe	chaff		consul
charted	chartered	councilor	counselor
chased	chaste	coup	coop
cheap	cheep	course	coarse
cheep	cheap	courtesy	curtsy
chili	chilly	creak	creek
choir	quire	crevasse	crevice
choose	chose	crochet	crotchet
	chosen	cue	queue
chord	cord	currant	current
chose	choose	curtsy	courtesy
	chosen	cygnet	signet
chute	shoot	cymbal	symbol
cite	sight	dairy	diary
	site	dam	damn
clothes	cloths	dammed	damned
coarse	course	damn	dam
collage	college	dear	deer
coma	comma	decry	descry
come	came	deer	dear
comma	coma	delusion	allusion
complement	compliment		illusion
complementary	complimentary	dependant	dependent
concert	consort	deprecate	depreciate
confidant	confidante	descendant	descendent
	confident	descry	decry
conscience	conscientious	desert	dessert
	conscious	device	devise
consort	concert	devolution	evolution
consul	council	dew	due
	counsel		Jew
continual	continuous	diary	dairy
coop	coup	did	done
coral	corral	die	dye
cord	chord	died	dyed

dinghy	dingy	ensure	insure
disbelief	disbelieve	entomologist	etymologist
discus	discuss	envelop	envelope
doe	dough	epigram	epitaph
doily	dolly		epithet
done	did		
dough	doe	ere	err
draft	draught	erotic	erratic
dragon	dragoon	err	ere
draught	draft	erratic	erotic
drawn	drew	escapement	escarpment
drank	drunk	essay	assay
drew	drawn	etymologist	entomologist
driven	drove	evolution	devolution
drunk	drank	ewe	yew
			you
dual	duel	except	accept
dudgeon	dungeon	excess	access
due	dew	executioner	executor
	Jew	exercise	exorcise
duel	dual	expand	expend
dully	duly	expansive	expensive
dye	die	expatiate	expiate
dyed	died	expend	expand
dyeing	dying	expensive	expansive
earthly	earthy	expiate	expatiate
easterly	eastern	extant	extinct
eaten	ate	eyrie	eerie
eclipse	ellipse	faint	feint
economic	economical	fair	fare
edition	addition	fallen	fell
eerie	eyrie		felled
effect	affect		
effluent	affluent	fare	fair
elder	eldest	fate	fête
elicit	illicit	faun	fawn
eligible	legible	feat	feet
ellipse	eclipse	feint	faint
elude	allude	fell	fallen
emend	amend		felled
emigrant	immigrant	ferment	foment
emigration	immigration	fête	fate
emission	omission	fiancé	fiancée
emphasis	emphasize	filed	filled
employee	employer	final	finale
		fir	fur

fission	fissure	franc	frank
flair	flare	freeze	frieze
flammable	inflammable	froze	frozen
flare	flair	funeral	funereal
flea	flee	fur	fir
flew	flu	gabble	gable
	flue	gaff	gaffe
flew	flown	gait	gate
flocks	phlox	galleon	gallon
floe	flow	gamble	gambol
flour	flower	gate	gait
floury	flowery	gave	given
flow	floe	genie	genius
flower	flour		genus
flowery	floury	genteel	gentile
flown	flew		gentle
flu	flew	genus	genie
	flue		genius
foment	ferment	gild	guild
font	fount	gilt	guilt
forbade	forbidden	given	gave
fore	four	glacier	glazier
foregone	forgone	goal	gaol
foresaw	foreseen	gone	went
foreword	forward	gorilla	guerrilla
forgave	forgiven	gourmand	gourmet
forgone	foregone	gradation	graduation
forgone	forwent	grate	great
forgot	forgotten	grew	grown
forsaken	forsook	grief	grieve
forswore	forsworn	grill	grille
fort	forte	griped	gripped
	forty	grisly	gristly
forth	fourth		grizzly
forty	fort	grope	group
	forte	ground	grounded
forward	foreword	grown	grew
forwent	forgone	guerrilla	gorilla
foul	fowl	guild	gild
found	founded	guilt	gilt
fount	font	hail	hale
four	fore	hair	hare
fourth	forth	half	halve
fowl	foul	hallo	hallow

	halo	impetuous	impetus
halve	half	impracticable	impractical
hangar	hanger	inapt	inept
hanged	hung	incredible	incredulous
hanger	hangar	indigenous	indigent
hare	hair	industrial	industrious
hart	heart	ineligible	illegible
heal	heel	inept	inapt
hear	here	inflammable	flammable
heart	hart	ingenious	ingenuous
heel	heal	inhuman	inhumane
heir	air	insure	ensure
here	hear	intelligent	intelligible
heron	herring	interment	internment
hew	hue	invertebrate	inveterate
hewed	hewn	jam	jamb
hid	hidden	Jew	dew
higher	hire	jib	due
him	hymn	jib	jibe
hire	higher	judicial	judicious
hoard	horde	junction	juncture
hoarse	horse	key	quay
hole	whole	knave	nave
honorary	honorable	knead	kneed
hoop	whoop		need
hoped	hopped	knew	known
horde	hoard	knew	new
horse	hoarse	knight	night
hue	hew	knightly	nightly
human	humane	knit	nit
humiliation	humility	knot	not
hung	hanged	knotty	naughty
hymn	him	know	no
idle	idol	known	knew
illegible	ineligible	lade	laid
illicit	elicit	lay	lied
illiterate	alliterate	lain	lane
illusion	allusion	lair	layer
	delusion	lama	llama
immigrant	emigrant	lane	lain
immigration	emigration	laterally	latterly
immoral	amoral	lath	lathe
	immortal	latterly	laterally
immorality	immortality	lay	lied

layer	lair	male	mail
lea	lee	mane	main
lead	led	maniac	manic
leak	leek	manner	manor
led	lead	mare	mayor
lee	lea	marina	merino
leek	leak	marshal	martial
legible	eligible	marten	martin
lemming	lemon	martial	marshal
leopard	leper	martin	marten
lessen	lesson	mask	masque
liable	libel	mat	matt, matte
liar	lyre	mayor	mare
libel	liable	maze	maize
lied	lay	mean	mien
lightening	lightning	meat	meet
lineament	liniment		mete out
liqueur	liquor	medal	meddle
literal	literary	mediate	meditate
	literate	meet	meat
llama	lama		mete out
load	lode	merino	marina
loan	lone	metal	mettle
loath	loathe	mete out	meat
local	locale		meet
lode	load	meter	meter
lone	loan	mettle	metal
looped	loped	mews	muse
	lopped	mien	mean
loose	lose	might	mite
loot	lute	miner	minor
loped	lopped	missal	missile
	looped	mistaken	mistook
lose	loose	mite	might
lumbar	lumber	moat	mote
lute	loot	modal	model
lyre	liar		module
macaroni	macaroon	momentary	momentous
made	maid		momentum
magnate	magnet	moose	mouse
maid	made		mousse
mail	male	moped	moped
main	mane	[mohpt]	[moh-ped]
maize	maze	moral	morale

morality	mortality	overtaken	overtook
mote	moat	overthrew	overthrown
motif	motive	packed	pact
mouse	moose	pail	pale
	mousse	pain	pane
mucous	mucus	pair	pare
multiple	multiply		pear
muscle	mussel	palate	palette
muse	mews		pallet
mussel	muscle	pale	pail
mystic	mystique	palette	palate
naught	nought		pallet
naughty	knotty	pane	pain
naval	navel	pare	pear
nave	knave		pair
navel	naval	passed	past
nay	née	pastel	pastille
	neigh	pate	pâté
need	knead		patty
	kneed	peace	piece
negligent	negligible	peak	peek
neigh	nay		pique
	née	peal	peel
new	knew	pear	pair
night	knight		pare
nightly	knightly	pearl	purl
nit	knit	peasant	pheasant
no	know	pedal	peddle
northerly	northern	peek	peak
not	knot		pique
nougat	nugget	peel	peal
nought	naught	peer	pier
nugget	nougat	pence	pennies
oar	ore	pendant	pendent
of	off	pennies	pence
official	officious	perquisite	prerequisite
omission	emission	personal	personnel
oral	aural	petrel	petrol
ore	oar	pheasant	peasant
organism	orgasm	phlox	flocks
outdid	outdone	piazza	pizza
overcame	overcome	piece	peace
overdid	overdone	pier	peer
overran	overrun	pined	pinned

piped	pipped	purl	pearl
pique	peak	put	putt
	peek	quash	squash
pistil	pistol	quay	key
pizza	piazza	queue	cue
place	plaice	quiet	quite
plain	plane	quire	choir
plaintiff	plaintive	quite	quiet
plait	plate	radar	raider
plane	plain	raged	ragged
plate	plait	raider	radar
plum	plumb	rain	reign
politic	political		rein
pool	pull	raise	raze
poplar	popular	rampant	rampart
pore	pour	ran	run
pored	poured	rang	ringed
poser	poseur		rung
pour	pore	rap	wrap
poured	pored	raped	rapped
practicable	practical	rapped	rapt
pray	prey		wrapped
precede	proceed	rated	ratted
premier	première	raze	raise
prerequisite	perquisite	read	red
prey	pray	read	reed
price	prise	real	reel
	prize	red	read
principal	principle	reel	real
prise	price	refuge	refugee
	prize	regal	regale
private	privet	reign	rain
prize	prise		rein
	price	relief	relieve
proceed	precede	reproof	reprove
profit	prophet	respectful	respective
proof	prove	rest	wrest
property	propriety	retch	wretch
prophecy	prophesy	review	revue
prophet	profit	rhyme	rime
propriety	property	ridden	rode
prostate	prostrate	right	rite
prove	proof		write
pull	pool	rime	rhyme

ring	wring	seen	saw
ringed	rang	seen	scene
	rung	seer	sear
risen	rose		sere
rite	right		
	write	sell	cell
road	rode	sensual	sensuous
	rowed	sent	scent
rode	ridden	septic	scent
roe	row	sere	skeptic
role	roll		sear
rose	risen	serial	seer
rote	wrote	series	cereal
rough	ruff	sew	serious
rout	route		so
row	roe		sow
rowed	road	sewed	sewn
	rode	sewer	sower
ruff	rough	sewn	sewed
run	ran	sextant	sown
rung	wrung	shaken	sexton
rye	wry	shear	shook
sail	sale	sheared	sheer
salon	saloon		sheered
sang	sung	shelf	shorn
sank	sunk	shoe	shelve
	sunken	shook	shoo
savior	savor	shoot	shaken
saw	seen	shorn	chute
sawed	sawn		sheared
scared	scarred	showed	sheered
scene	seen	shrank	shown
scent	cent	sight	shrunk
	sent		cite
scraped	scrapped	signet	site
sculptor	sculpture	silicon	cygnet
sea	see	singeing	silicone
sealing	ceiling	sinuous	singing
seam	seem	site	sinus
sear	seer		cite
	sere	skeptic	sight
secret	secrete	skies	septic
see	sea	slain	skis
seem	seam	slated	slew
			slatted

slay	sleigh	step	steppe
slew	slain	stile	style
sloe	slow	stimulant	stimulus
sloped	slopped	stock	stalk
slow	sloe	stocked	stoked
smelled	smelt	straight	strait
sniped	snipped	straightened	straitened
so	sew	stratum	stratus
	sow	strewed	strewn
soar	sore	strife	strive
sociable	social	striped	stripped
solder	soldier	strive	strife
sole	soul	striven	strove
some	sum	stunk	stank
son	sun	sty	stye
soot	suit	style	stile
sore	soar	suede	swede
soul	sole	suit	soot
southerly	southern	suite	sweet
sow	sew	sum	some
	so	summary	summery
sowed	sown	sun	son
sower	sewer	sundae	Sunday
sown	sewn	sung	sang
spared	sparred	sunk	sank
species	specious		sunken
sped	speeded	super	supper
spoke	spoken	surplice	surplus
sprang	sprung	swam	swum
squash	quash	swede	suede
staid	stayed	sweet	suite
stair	stare	swelled	swollen
stake	steak	swollen	swelled
stalk	stock	swore	sworn
stanch	staunch	swum	swam
stank	stunk	symbol	cymbal
stare	stair	tacks	tax
starcd	starred	tail	tale
stationary	stationery	taken	took
statue	statute	tale	tail
staunch	stanch	taped	tapped
stayed	staid	taper	tapir
steak	stake	tapped	taped
steal	steel	tare	tear

taught	taut	trod	trodden
tax	tacks	troop	troupe
tea	tee	turban	turbine
team	teem	two	to
tear	tare		too
tear	tier	tycoon	typhoon
tee	tea	unaware	unawares
teem	team	unconscionable	unconscious
teeth	teethe	undid	undone
teethe	teeth	unwanted	unwonted
temporal	temporary	urban	urbane
tendon	tenon	vacation	vocation
tenor	tenure	vain	vane
testimonial	testimony		vein
their	there	vale	veil
	they're	venal	venial
thorough	through	veracity	voracity
thrash	thresh	vertex	vortex
threw	through	vigilant	vigilante
threw	thrown	vocation	vacation
throes	throws	voracity	veracity
throne	thrown	vortex	vertex
through	thorough	wafer	waver
through	threw	waged	wagged
thrown	throne	waif	waive
throws	throes		wave
thyme	time	waist	waste
tic	tick	want	wont
tier	tear	warden	warder
tiled	tilled	ware	wear
timber	timbre	waste	waist
time	thyme	wave	waif
to	too		waive
	two	waver	wafer
toe	tow	way	weigh
tomb	tome	weak	week
too	to	wear	ware
	two	weekly	weakly
took	taken	weigh	way
topi	toupee	went	gone
tore	torn	westerly	western
tow	toe	wet	whet
trait	tray	whit	wit
treaties	treatise	whole	hole

whoop	hoop		rapt
willed	would	wreak	wreck
winded	wound	wreath	wreathe
wit	whit	wrest	rest
withdrawn	withdrew	wretch	retch
wittily	wittingly	wring	ring
woe	woo	write	right
woke	woken		rite
wont	want	wrung	rung
woo	woe	wry	rye
wore	worn	wrote	rote
would	willed		written
would	wood	yew	ewe
	wooed		you
wove	woven	yoke	yolk
wrap	rap	yore	your
wrapped	rapped		